Level 1
STUDENT
BOOK
Units 1–6
LANGUAGE!® Live
YOU PICK
Resume Lesson 2
Give Feedback
100% COMPLETE
Profile
This Week
TRAINING TIME
POINTS EARNED
Your Notifications
Leaderboard
Progress
Unit Intro
VOYAGER SOPRIS
LEARNING®
Louisa Moats, Ed.D., Author

For a complete listing of copyright permission acknowledgements, please see p. 295.

8 9 10 11 HPS 24 23 22 21

978-1-62489-933-1
1-62489-933-1
323002

Printed in the United States of America

Published and Distributed by

VOYAGER SOPRIS
LEARNING®

17855 Dallas Parkway, Suite 400 • Dallas, TX 75287 • 800 547-6747
www.voyagersopris.com

Table of Contents

Unit 1 "Batty About Bats!"

Lesson 1 1
Lesson 2 6
Lesson 3 10
Lesson 4 16
Lesson 5 19
Lesson 6 23
Lesson 7 26
Lesson 8 28
Lesson 9 33
Lesson 10 34

Unit 2 "Africa Digs"

Lesson 1 41
Lesson 2 47
Lesson 3 51
Lesson 4 56
Lesson 5 60
Lesson 6 65
Lesson 7 68
Lesson 8 72
Lesson 9 77
Lesson 10 78

Unit 3 "Gemini: The Twins"

Lesson 1 83
Lesson 2 88
Lesson 3 92
Lesson 4 96
Lesson 5 100
Lesson 6 104
Lesson 7 107
Lesson 8 111
Lesson 9 116
Lesson 10 117

Unit 4 "Jazz: The Recipe"

Lesson 1 123
Lesson 2 127
Lesson 3 131
Lesson 4 135
Lesson 5 139
Lesson 6 143
Lesson 7 146
Lesson 8 150
Lesson 9 153
Lesson 10 155

Table of Contents (*cont.*)

Unit 5 "Coming Clean About Toxic Pollution"

Lesson 1 161
Lesson 2 166
Lesson 3 171
Lesson 4 178
Lesson 5 181
Lesson 6 186
Lesson 7 191
Lesson 8 195
Lesson 9 202
Lesson 10 210

Unit 6 "Censorship"

Lesson 1 215
Lesson 2 219
Lesson 3 225
Lesson 4 230
Lesson 5 235
Lesson 6 240
Lesson 7 246
Lesson 8 249
Lesson 9 252
Lesson 10 256

Additional Resources

Unit Passages 263
Graphic Organizers
Fluency Charts 283
Key Passage Vocabulary 287
Multiple-Meaning Map 288
Four-Square 289
Define It 291
Blueprint for Writing 292

Let's Focus: "Batty About Bats!"

Content Focus
bats

Type of Text
informational

Big Ideas
Consider the following Big Idea questions. Write your answer for each question.

How are bats useful to humans?

____

____

____

How are humans impacting bats?

____

____

____

Reading for a Purpose

1. Is a bat a mammal?
2. Are all bats bug eaters?
3. Are bats blind?
4. Are bats able to "see" with sound?
5. Are colonies where bats live?
6. Are bats helpful to farmers?
7. Are bats in danger?

Text Features

Informational text gives facts or information. Writers of **informational text** use **text features** to provide clues to the topic and other important information.

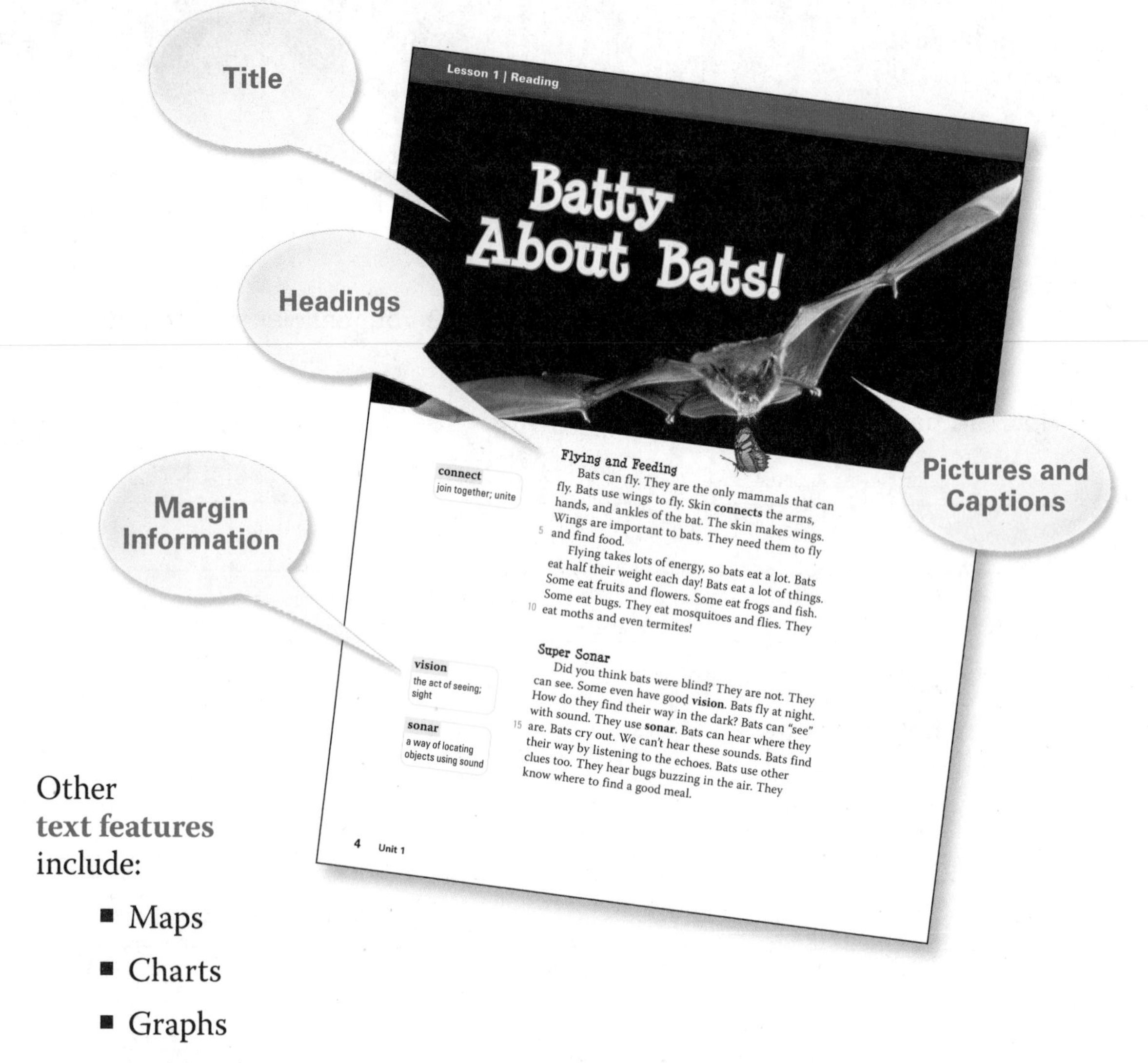

Other **text features** include:

- Maps
- Charts
- Graphs
- Bold words
- Highlighted words

Key Passage Vocabulary: "Batty About Bats!"

Rate your knowledge of the words. Define the words. Draw a picture to help you remember the definition.

Vocabulary	Knowledge Rating	Definition	Picture
connect	0 1 2 3		
vision	0 1 2 3		
sonar	0 1 2 3		
colony	0 1 2 3		
danger	0 1 2 3		
interfere	0 1 2 3		
ignorance	0 1 2 3		
negligence	0 1 2 3		

Batty About Bats!

Flying and Feeding

connect
join together; unite

Bats can fly. They are the only mammals that can fly. Bats use wings to fly. Skin **connects** the arms, hands, and ankles of the bat. The skin makes wings. Wings are important to bats. They need them to fly 5 and find food.

Flying takes lots of energy, so bats eat a lot. Bats eat half their weight each day! Bats eat a lot of things. Some eat fruits and flowers. Some eat frogs and fish. Some eat bugs. They eat mosquitoes and flies. They 10 eat moths and even termites!

Super Sonar

vision
the act of seeing; sight

sonar
a way of locating objects using sound

Did you think bats were blind? They are not. They can see. Some even have good **vision**. Bats fly at night. How do they find their way in the dark? Bats can "see" with sound. They use **sonar**. Bats can hear where they 15 are. Bats cry out. We can't hear these sounds. Bats find their way by listening to the echoes. Bats use other clues too. They hear bugs buzzing in the air. They know where to find a good meal.

The Marianas flying fox eats fruit.

Hanging Out and Helping

Bats hang out. They hang upside down when they
20 sleep. Some bats live in trees or buildings. Some bats live in caves. Millions of bats can live in one cave. Groups of bats living together are called bat **colonies**.

Bats "go to bat" for the Earth. Bats eat a lot of bugs. They save the plants that bugs like to eat. Without bats,
25 bugs could kill a lot of plants. Farmers could lose their farms. Millions of people would be hungry.

Bats also help plants grow. They scatter seeds. There is a fruit in Asia. It is a crop that brings in millions of dollars. What if there were no bats? This
30 plant could not grow. Farmers would lose cash.

colony
group of animals or people living together

Bats in Trouble

Today, bats are in **danger** from us. We destroy their homes. We **interfere** in their colonies. Some people have plans to help the bats. One plan shuts gates to old mines. This keeps people out, but it lets bats in. Some
35 chemicals kill bats. There is a plan to stop using these chemicals. These plans help everyone.

Scientists teach us about bats. Others help bats live. They count bat colonies. They study bats. What can you do for bats?

40 "There is no point in finding out more about these creatures if we destroy them with **ignorance** and **negligence**," says one expert. "Bats need friends!"

Adapted with permission from "Batty About Bats!"
by Kathiann M. Kowalski

danger
a condition in which something bad or harmful could happen

interfere
to get in the way of; disturb

ignorance
lack of knowledge

negligence
lack of care

A vampire bat goes for a "walk."

Multiple-Meaning Map

Determine the meanings of the word *bat*. Write the definitions in the boxes. Use the word in a sentence on the lines below the boxes.

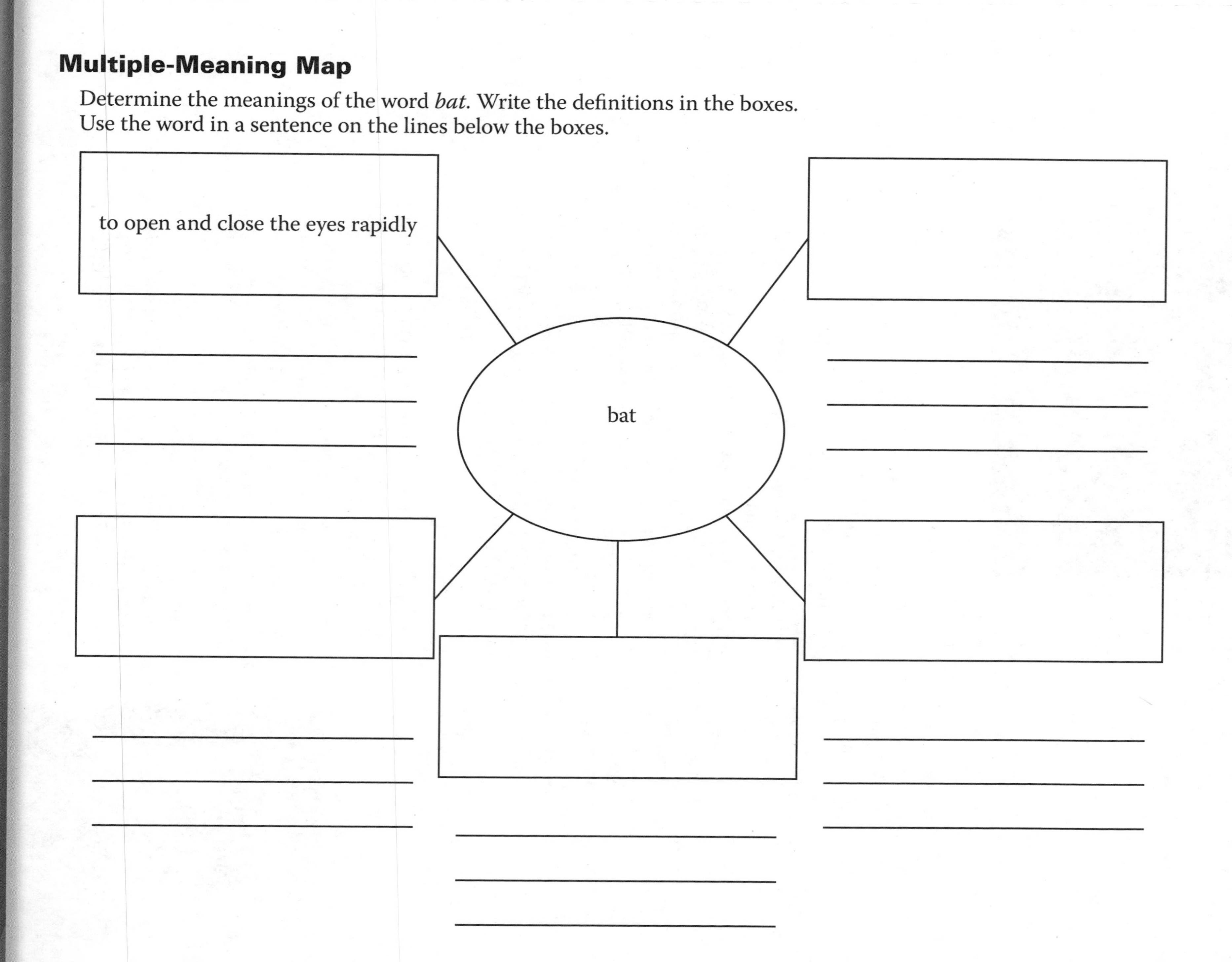

Nouns

When we understand words and their meanings, we can use them in sentences. Words have different functions in sentences. Sometimes the same word can have different functions depending on how it is used.

What Is a Noun?

A **noun** is the naming part of a sentence. It answers the question *who* or *what.*

The **cat** sat.

The **man** dreams.

The **fish** swims.

Sam hops.

Sally thinks.

The **pants** are green.

The **sun** is hot.

The **bat** flies.

The **player** hits.

Find It: Nouns

Part A

Read the excerpt. Find the nouns—words that name *who* or *what.* Underline the nouns.

Based on "Batty About Bats!"

Bats fly. Bats have extra skin. This skin connects their hands, arms, and ankles. The skin forms wings. Bats use wings to fly. Bats fly at night to find food. Bats need wings to eat.

People sit and stand. Bats hang upside down, even while sleeping. Some bats live in trees. Some bats live in buildings. Other bats live in caves.

Part B

Sort the nouns into the correct columns.

Who	What

Basic Punctuation

Part A

Read the sentences. Circle all punctuation marks. Underline all capital letters.

1. Bats use wings to fly. Skin connects the arms, hands, and ankles of the bat.

2. Flying takes lots of energy, so bats eat a lot. Bats eat half their weight each day!

3. Bats eat a lot of bugs. They save the plants that bugs like to eat. Without bats, bugs could kill a lot of plants.

4. There is a fruit in Asia. It is a crop that brings in millions of dollars. What if there were no bats?

5. Today, bats are in danger from us. We destroy their homes.

Part B

Read the paragraph. Add the missing punctuation marks to the end of the sentences as well as inside the sentences. Triple underline the first letter of a word that needs capitalizing.

bats fly at night did you know that they use sonar
to see at night they eat all night long after flying all
night they are tired they sleep in caves in bushes
and even in buildings bats can be found flying
eating and sleeping all over the united states

Word Fluency

Read the words fluently.

	Correct	Errors
1st Try		
2nd Try		

pan	fat	man	tap	map	sat	mat	can	pat	tan	10
man	mat	pat	map	tap	fat	sat	tan	can	pat	20
mat	map	tap	sat	can	tan	pat	fat	pat	man	30
sat	tap	mat	fat	pat	man	tan	pan	map	can	40
can	map	tan	pat	mat	tap	fat	can	sat	pan	50
pat	pan	can	fat	map	mat	tan	tap	man	sat	60
tan	pat	man	fat	pan	can	map	sat	mat	tap	70
man	pan	fat	sat	pat	tan	tap	map	can	mat	80
fat	sat	tap	man	map	sat	pat	mat	pat	pan	90
map	tap	sat	mat	map	fat	can	pan	tan	man	100

Sort It: Meaning Categories

Sort these words into categories. Some words fit in two categories.

Word Bank

~~boy~~	~~bat~~	man	plant	you
raft	pant	map	mat	plan
map	mat	plan	cat	stamp
Sam	I	pan	ran	jam

Living Things	Actions	Things That Are Flat
boy	bat	
bat		

Verbs

Verbs are the doing part of a sentence. Verbs describe actions.

We **can see** some actions:

jump, walk, and clap

Some actions we **can't see**:

think, wish, and dream

The boy **runs**.

Pat **plans** a trip.

The girl **reads**.

Sam **bats**.

The bug **flies**.

The man **hopes**.

The dog **eats**.

The bear **hunts**.

Stan **thinks**.

Find It: Verbs

Part A

Read the sentences. Find the verb—the word that answers: *What did they (he, she, it) do?*

Circle the verbs.

1. Bats fly.
2. Sam bats the ball.
3. Bats catch food at night.
4. People sit.
5. Bats hang in trees.
6. Some bats live in caves.
7. Cats stand.
8. Bats eat bugs.
9. Bats help crops.
10. The bats scatter seeds.

Part B

Copy the words into the correct columns.

Can See the Action	Can't See the Action

Question Words

How to Answer Questions

Use these steps to answer a short-answer question with a complete sentence:

1. Look for a question word to know what the question is asking.
2. Find information in the text to answer the question.
3. Plan and write the answer.
4. Check the answer.

Example question:

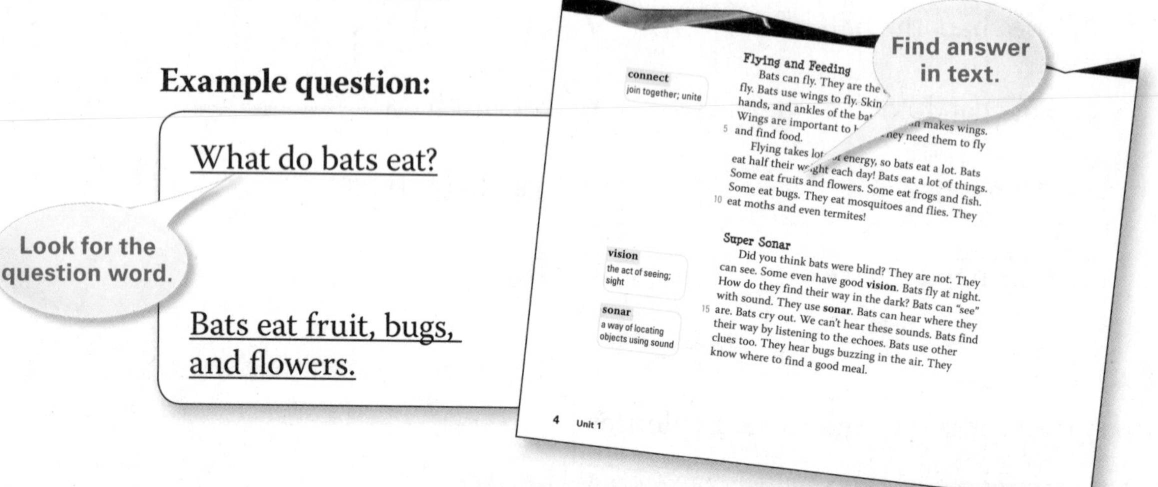

connect
join together; unite

Flying and Feeding

Bats can fly. They are the
fly. Bats use wings to fly. Skin
hands, and ankles of the ba
Wings are important to
n makes wings.
ney need them to fly
5 and find food.

Flying takes lot energy, so bats eat a lot. Bats
eat half their weight each day! Bats eat a lot of things.
Some eat fruits and flowers. Some eat frogs and fish.
Some eat bugs. They eat mosquitoes and flies. They
10 eat moths and even termites!

vision
the act of seeing; sight

sonar
a way of locating objects using sound

Super Sonar

Did you think bats were blind? They are not. They
can see. Some even have good **vision**. Bats fly at night.
How do they find their way in the dark? Bats can "see"
with sound. They use **sonar**. Bats can hear where they
15 are. Bats cry out. We can't hear these sounds. Bats find
their way by listening to the echoes. Bats use other
clues too. They hear bugs buzzing in the air. They
know where to find a good meal.

4 Unit 1

Question words help you know how to answer the question.

Question Words	How to Answer
If the question asks . . .	Your answer must include . . .
Who	information about a person or group
What	an action or name of a thing
When	a specific time, date, or event
Where	a general location or specific place

Question Words	How to Answer
If the question asks . . .	Your answer must include . . .
Is/Are	a "yes" or a "no" answer plus explanation
Do/Does	a "yes" or a "no" answer plus explanation

Question Words	How to Answer
If the question asks . . .	Your answer must include . . .
Why	a reason or explanation
How	the way something is done

Question Words

Determine the question word and write it above the picture.
Then, write a question on the lines below the picture.

Phrase Fluency

Read each phrase fluently.

	Correct	Errors
1st Try		
2nd Try		

Phrase	Count	Phrase	Count
at the bat	3	my pal Pam	75
have a tan	6	on the cap	78
Sam sat	8	one fat cat	81
Sal sat	10	have a nap	84
on the mat	13	on the map	87
am last	15	by the cab	90
on the lap	18	have a sip	93
tap the sap	21	by the van	96
have a pan	24	in the cab	99
a man	26	by the rim	102
ran a lap	29	is a fan	105
cap the can	32	in the van	108
can nap	34	by the man	111
I am	36	sat by Jim	114
on the mat	39	in the bin	117
have a cap	42	on the mat	120
can I have	45	a cat nap	123
can I pat	48	in the can	126
the tan cat	51	fan the man	129
the fat cat	54	in a jam	132
ran a lap	57	pat the man	135
by my fan	60	the tan man	138
jab at the rat	64	a cat pin	141
the one on the mat	69	the can rim	144
my tan bat	72	on the tan mat	148

Sentence Morphs

Read the phrases. Scoop them in the complete sentences.

the mats are in the cab The mats are in the cab.	Tam has a fat cat Tam has a fat cat.	Sam is at bat Sam is at bat.
the cat is fat The cat is fat.	I am at bat I am at bat.	I am Tam I am Tam.
Mac has the bats in the cab Mac has the bats in the cab.	Mac has the mat Mac has the mat.	Tam sat in the cab Tam sat in the cab.

Sentence Morph Tic-Tac-Toe

Read the chunks, then read the sentence. Once read correctly, claim the square. Try to claim three squares in a row.

I slam the last mat I slam the last mat.	the tam is on Sal The tam is on Sal.	Sam has a cat Sam has a cat.
I slam it on the mat I slam it on the mat.	I am on the mat I am on the mat.	Sal is on the mat Sal is on the mat.
that mat is last That mat is last.	Sam sat on the mat Sam sat on the mat.	I am last I am last.

Define It

Determine the category and attributes of each word. Then, write the definition.

Word		Category		Attributes
mammal	=	animal	+	has fur; warm-blooded; has live births; feeds its babies milk; breathes air

Definition:
A mammal is a warm-blooded animal that has fur, delivers live babies, feeds its babies milk, and breathes air.

Word		Category		Attributes
chemicals	=		+	

Definition:

Word		Category		Attributes
termite	=		+	

Definition:

Word		Category		Attributes
mosquito	=		+	

Definition:

Close Reading: Guided Highlighting

Read the text and complete the tasks.

Batty About Bats!

Flying and Feeding

Bats can fly. They are the only mammals that can fly. Bats use wings to fly. Skin **connects** the arms, hands, and ankles of the bat. The skin makes wings. Wings are important to bats. They need them to fly and find food.

Flying takes lots of energy, so bats eat a lot. Bats eat half their weight each 5 day! Bats eat a lot of things. Some eat fruits and flowers. Some eat frogs and fish. Some eat bugs. They eat mosquitoes and flies. They eat moths and even termites!

- **What is the section mostly about?** Finish the sentence below.

  Flying and Feeding tells how ______________________________

  ______________________________.

Super Sonar

Did you think bats were blind? They are not. They can see. Some even have good **vision**. Bats fly at night. How do they find their way in the 10 dark? Bats can "see" with sound. They use **sonar**. Bats can hear where they are. Bats cry out. We can't hear these sounds. Bats find their way by listening to the echoes. Bats use other clues too. They hear bugs buzzing in the air. They know where to find a good meal.

- **What is the section mostly about?** Finish the sentence below.

  Super Sonar explains ______________________________

  ______________________________.

Close Reading: Guided Highlighting (*cont.*)

Hanging Out and Helping

Bats hang out. They hang upside down when they sleep. Some bats live in
15 trees or buildings. Some bats live in caves. Millions of bats can live in one cave. Groups of bats living together are called bat **colonies**.

Bats "go to bat" for the Earth. Bats eat a lot of bugs. They save the plants that bugs like to eat. Without bats, bugs could kill a lot of plants. Farmers could lose their farms. Millions of people would be hungry.

20 Bats also help plants grow. They scatter seeds. There is a fruit in Asia. It is a crop that brings in millions of dollars. What if there were no bats? This plant could not grow. Farmers would lose cash.

- **What is the section mostly about?** Finish the sentence below. (Hint: Where do they live? How do they help?)

  Hanging Out and Helping describes ______________________________

  ____

  ______________________________.

Bats in Trouble

Today, bats are in **danger** from us. We destroy their homes. We **interfere** in their colonies. Some people have plans to help the bats. One plan
25 shuts gates to old mines. This keeps people out, but it lets bats in. Some chemicals kill bats. There is a plan to stop using these chemicals. These plans help everyone.

Scientists teach us about bats. Others help bats live. They count bat colonies. They study bats. What can you do for bats?

30 "There is no point in finding out more about these creatures if we destroy them with **ignorance** and **negligence**," says one expert. "Bats need friends!"

- **What is the section mostly about?** Fill in the blanks to answer the question. Humans put ______________ in danger. We destroy their ______________ and disturb their ______________. Scientists are trying to help bats ______________.

Masterpiece Sentences

Use the pictures to write Stage 1 sentences.

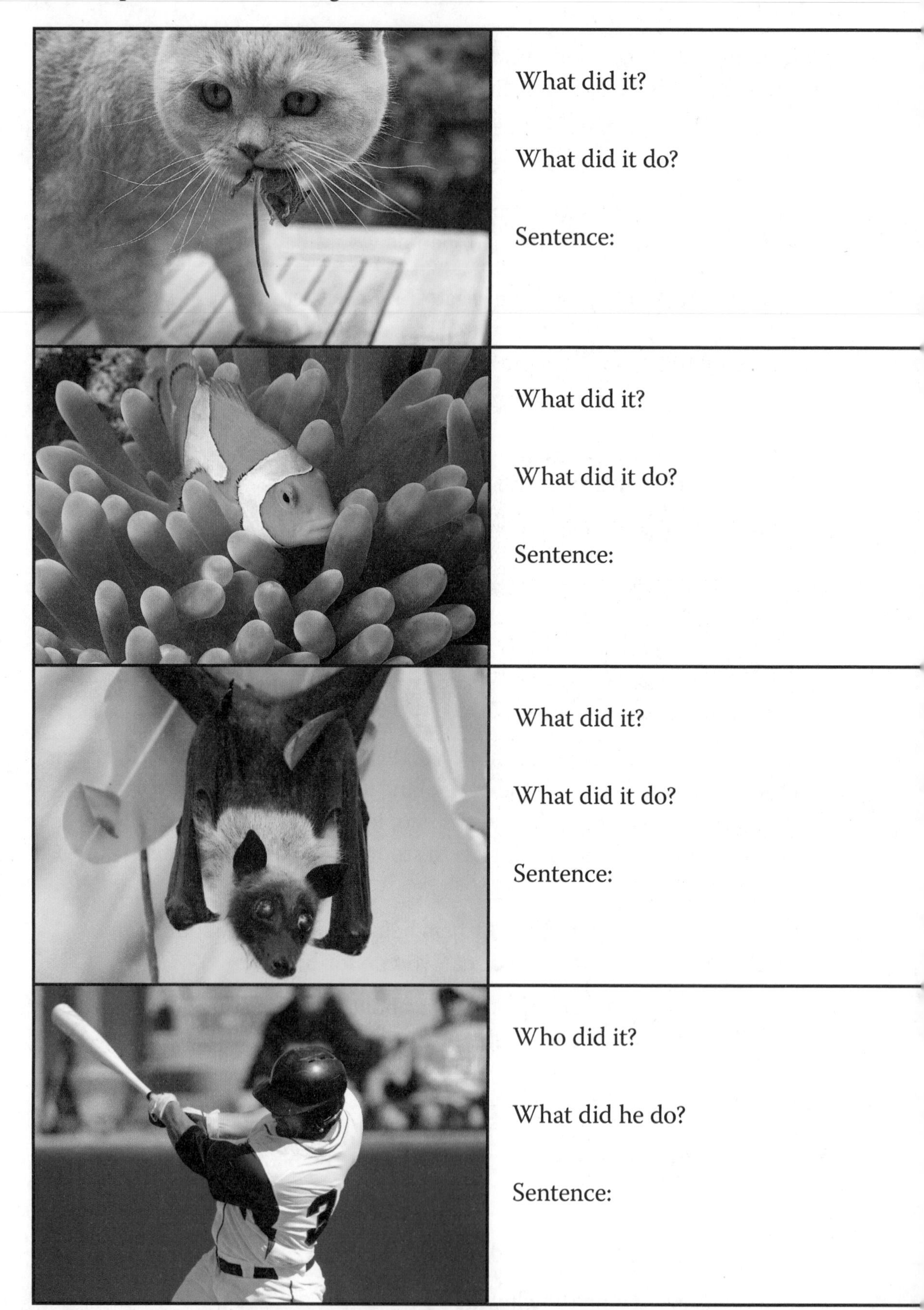

What did it?

What did it do?

Sentence:

What did it?

What did it do?

Sentence:

What did it?

What did it do?

Sentence:

Who did it?

What did he do?

Sentence:

Ask and Answer Questions

Question words help you know how to ask and answer a question.

Question Words	How to Answer
If the question asks . . .	**Your answer must include . . .**
Who	information about a person or group
What	an action or name of a thing
Where	a general location or specific place
When	a time, date, or event
Is/Are/ Do/Does	a "yes" or a "no" answer plus explanation

Ask About It!

Write questions for each section of the passage "Batty About Bats!" Use the question words to help you.

Flying and Feeding *Is/Are?* *What?*

1. ____

Super Sonar *Is/Are?* *When?*

2. ____

Hanging Out and Helping *Do/Does?* *Where?*

3. ____

Bats in Trouble *Do/Does?* *Who?*

4. ____

Passage Comprehension

Underline the question word in each question. Then, answer each question using a complete sentence. Underline the part of the answer that replaces the question word. Write the evidence from the text.

1. Is a bat a mammal?

   ____

   Text Evidence: ______________________________

2. Are all bats bug eaters?

   ____

   Text Evidence: ______________________________

3. Are bats blind?

   ____

   Text Evidence: ______________________________

4. Are bats able to "see" with sound?

   ____

   Text Evidence: ______________________________

5. Are colonies where bats live?

   ____

   Text Evidence: ______________________________

6. Are bats helpful to farmers?

   ____

   Text Evidence: ______________________________

   ____

7. Are bats in danger?

   ____

   Text Evidence: ______________________________

   ____

Four-Square

Write the definition of *interfere*. Then, write examples of the word in the appropriate box.

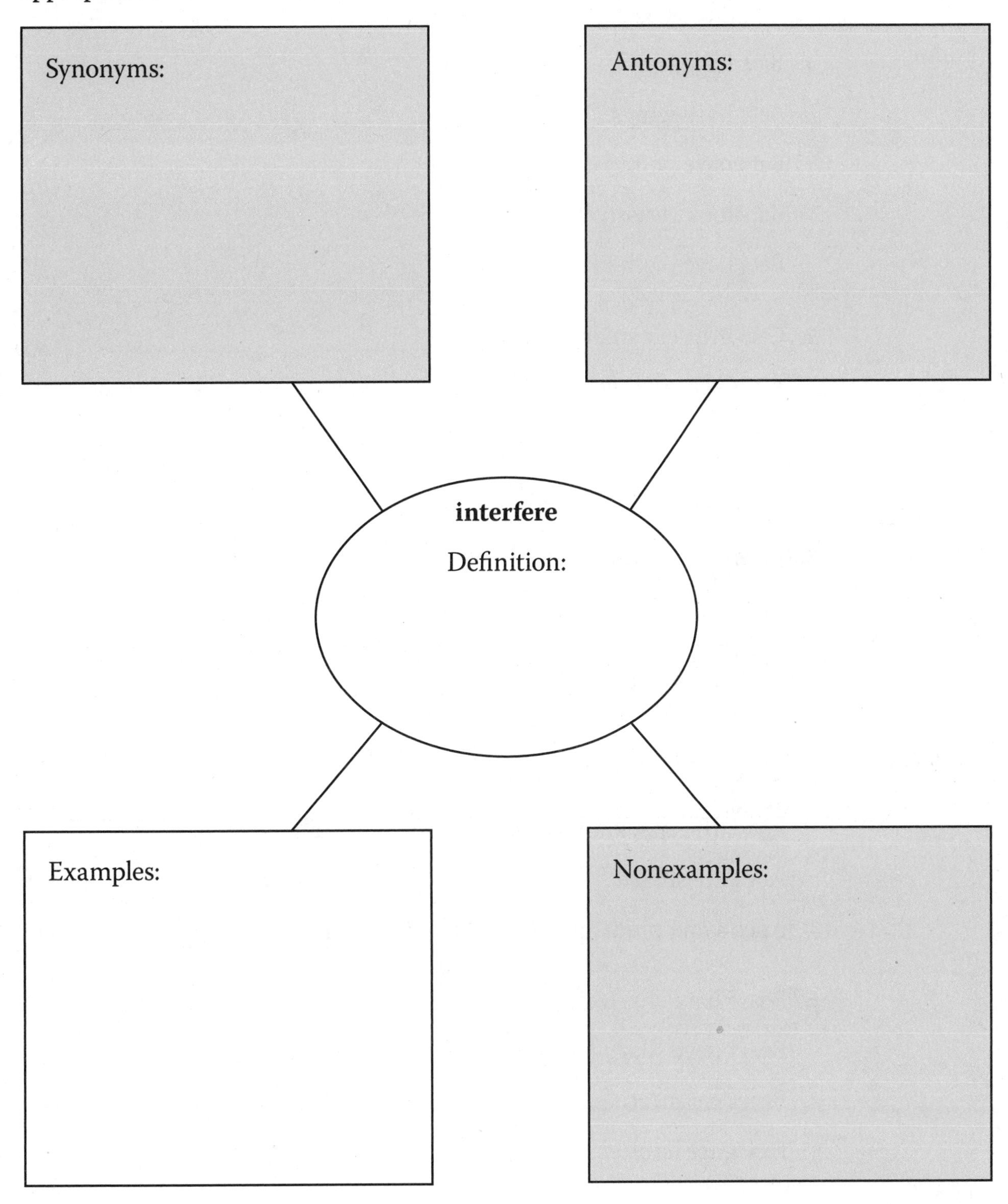

Identify It: Main Idea

Read each group of sentences below. Identify one sentence that tells what all of the sentences are about. Circle that sentence. That is the main idea.

1. Bats have fur.

   Bats have wings.

   Bats have pointy ears.

   Bats look very strange.

   Bats have teeth like rats.

2. Cats are very smart.

   A cat is a good pet.

   A cat can do tricks.

   It is easy to care for a cat.

3. Tigers live in the jungle.

   Tigers eat other animals.

   Tigers sleep on the ground.

   Tigers are wild!

4. Apes use sticks to find food.

   Koko, the ape, knows several letters of the alphabet.

   Apes are smart.

   Apes avoid predators by swinging in the trees.

5. Bears have sharp claws.

   Bears have sharp teeth.

   Bears eat meat.

   Bears are hunters.

Write It: Main Idea

Read the sentence frame. Read each group of three key details. Then, complete the sentence frame to tell how the details are related. This sentence tells the main idea for the group of key details.

1. Casey is ______________________________.

   Casey can run fast.

   Casey can hit a ball very far.

   Casey can pitch and catch.

2. A dog is ______________________________.

   A dog will fetch the newspaper.

   A dog will protect you from harm.

   A dog is always happy to see you.

3. My cat is ______________________________.

   My cat has pretty green eyes.

   My cat moves with grace.

   My cat is as black as night!

4. A snake is ______________________________.

   A snake does not feed its babies milk.

   A snake is not warm-blooded.

   A snake does not have fur.

5. An elephant is ______________________________.

   An elephant breathes air.

   An elephant has fur.

   An elephant feeds milk to its babies.

Word Fluency

Read the words fluently.

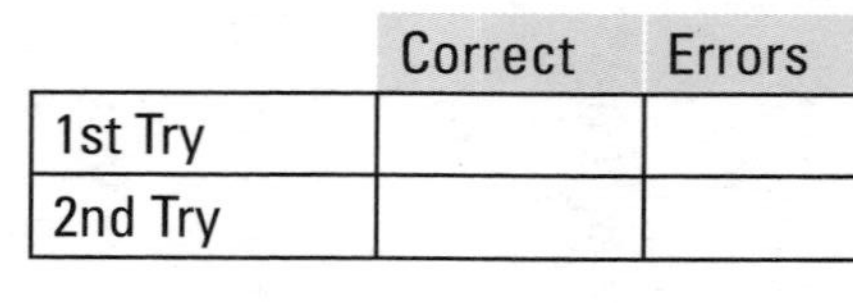

	Correct	Errors
1st Try		
2nd Try		

pan	fat	man	tap	map	sat	mat	can	pat	tan	10
man	mat	pat	map	tap	fat	sat	tan	can	pat	20
mat	map	tap	sat	can	tan	pat	fat	pat	man	30
sat	tap	mat	fat	pat	man	tan	pan	map	can	40
can	map	tan	pat	mat	tap	fat	can	sat	pan	50
pat	pan	can	fat	map	mat	tan	tap	man	sat	60
tan	pat	man	fat	pan	can	map	sat	mat	tap	70
man	pan	fat	sat	pat	tan	tap	map	can	mat	80
fat	sat	tap	man	map	sat	pat	mat	pat	pan	90
map	tap	sat	mat	map	fat	can	pan	tan	man	100

Diagram It: Subject and Predicate

Fill in the diagrams using information from the pictures. Use the diagrams to say a complete sentence.

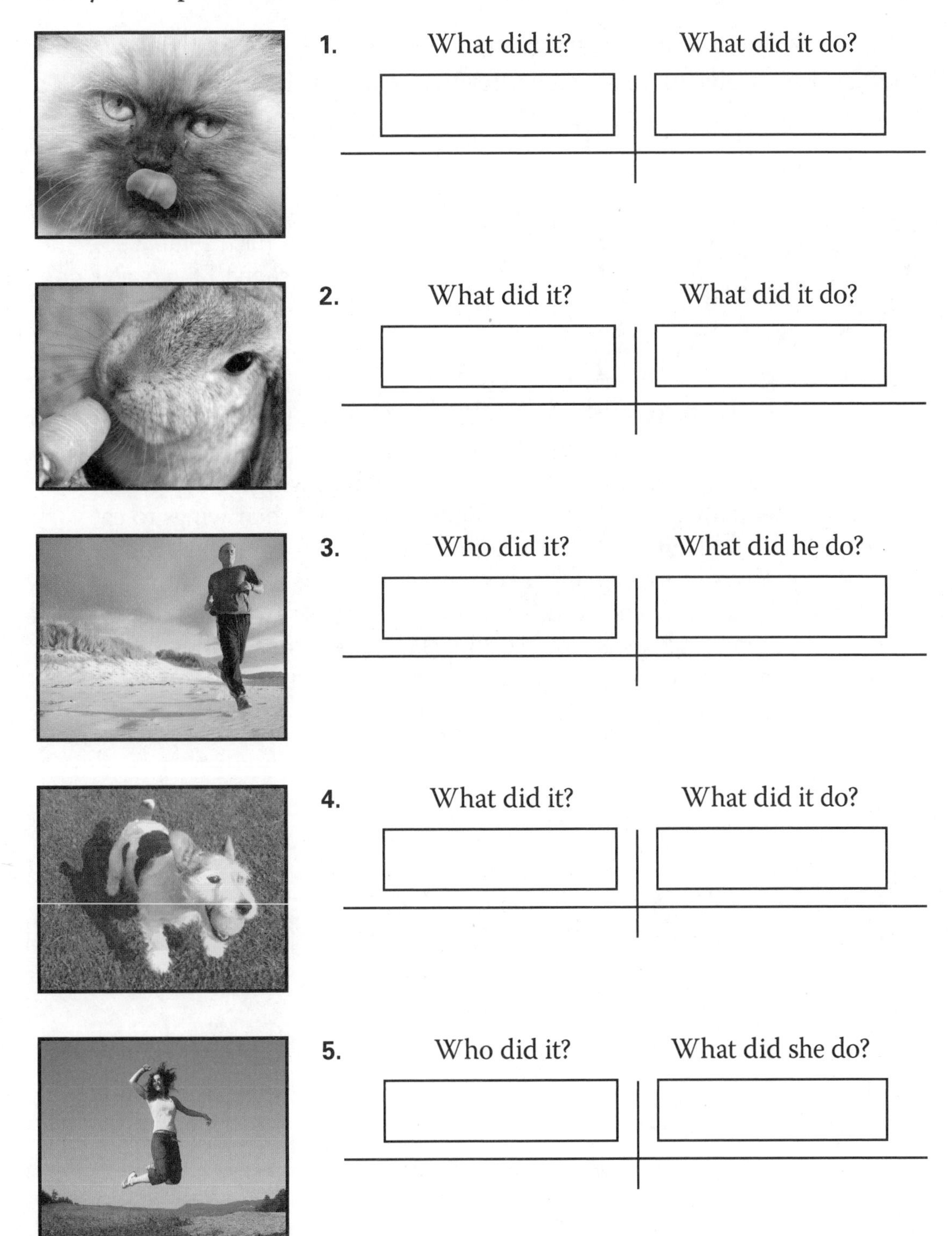

Text Structure

Well-written text has organization. Informational text is organized using main ideas and supporting details.

The main idea tells what the paragraph is about.
The key details give more specific information about the main idea.

Ask yourself...
Which sentence tells what all of the sentences are about?

Ask yourself...
Which sentences support the main idea?

The bat can fly. It is the only mammal that can fly. Bats use wings to fly. Skin connects parts of the bat. It joins its hands, arms, and ankles. The skin makes wings. Bats fly to look for food. They fly at night. They need their wings to eat.

Bats eat a lot. Bats eat half their weight each day! Food makes energy. Flying takes energy. Bats eat a lot of things. Some eat fruits. Some eat flowers. Some eat frogs and fish. Some eat lizards. Some eat bugs. They eat mosquitoes. They eat flies. They eat moths. They even eat termites!

Blueprint for Reading: Main Idea

Highlight the **main ideas** in green. Highlight the **key details** in yellow.

Based on "Batty About Bats!"

Flying and Feeding

The bat can fly. It is the only mammal that can fly. Bats use wings to fly. Skin connects parts of the bat. It joins its hands, arms, and ankles. The skin makes wings. Bats fly to look for food. They fly at night. They need their wings to eat.

Bats eat a lot. Bats eat half their weight each day! Food makes energy. Flying takes energy. Bats eat a lot of things. Some eat fruits. Some eat flowers. Some eat frogs and fish. Some eat lizards. Some eat bugs. They eat mosquitoes. They eat flies. They eat moths. They even eat termites!

Super Sonar

Bats "see" with sound. They use sonar. Bats can hear where they are. They cry out. The sound comes back. It echoes. We can't hear these sounds. But bats can. Bats use other sound clues too. Bugs buzz around. Bats hear them. Lots of bugs mean lots of food.

Blueprint for Reading: Main Idea (*cont.*)

Based on "Batty About Bats!"

Hanging Out and Helping

Bats hang. They hang upside down. They hang when they sleep. Bats hang where they live. Bats live in trees. Bats live in buildings. Bats live in caves. Many live in one cave. These are bat colonies.

Bats "go to bat" for the Earth. They eat a lot of bugs. Bugs kill plants. Farmers could lose their farms. Millions would be hungry. Bats help plants. They scatter seeds. Think about this. There is a fruit in Asia. It makes millions in cash. What if there were no bats? This plant could not grow. It could not spread. Farmers would lose the fruit. They would lose the cash.

Bats in Trouble

Today, bats are in danger. People hurt their homes. We interfere in their colonies. We use chemicals.

Blueprint for Writing: Main Idea

Write the main ideas and key details to help you retell the passage and write a summary.

Using New Vocabulary

Fill in the blanks with the appropriate vocabulary words. If you need assistance, use the word bank at the bottom of the page.

Bats are the only mammals with wings. Skin ____________ their hands to their feet to make the wings. Many people think that bats are blind, but they actually have good ____________. Bats fly at night, so it is difficult to see. Bats find their way in the dark using ____________. Bats live under bridges, in trees, and in caves. Many bats live together in a bat ____________. Humans often fear bats because of ____________. This causes them to ____________ with bat homes and disrupt their lives. Bats are in ____________, and many humans do not care. This ____________ will eventually cause problems with our ecosystem.

Word Bank

interfere	ignorance	sonar	negligence
colony	vision	danger	connects

Sort It: Main Idea and Key Details

Determine the main idea and key details of "Batty About Bats!"

Main Ideas	Details

Bats save plants from bugs.	Bats have an oddly shaped nose.	Humans hurt bats.
Bats have fur and wings.	People interfere with bat colonies.	Bats help farmers.
Humans destroy their homes.	Scientists teach about bats.	Scientists help bats.
Bats have sharp claws.	Bats scatter seeds.	Bats are strange.
People use harsh chemicals.	Scientists count bat colonies.	Scientists study bats.
Bats help plants grow.	Bats have teeth like rats.	

Masterpiece Sentences Tic-Tac-Toe

For each topic, place two sentence parts in the square. Read the complete sentence to claim the square. Try to claim three squares in a row.

Nocturnal bat	Flying fox	Groups of bats
Hungry bat	Scientists	Farmers
Ignorant humans	Insect-eating bats	Chemicals

Masterpiece Sentences Tic-Tac-Toe (*cont.*)

Cut out the strips and use with the Masterpiece Sentences Tic-Tac-Toe board.

Who or What did it?	What did they do?
the nocturnal bat	ate the butterfly
the flying fox	live in colonies
groups of bats	need bats
the hungry bat	count bat colonies
scientists	flew at night
farmers	ate the fruit
ignorant humans	kill bats
insect-eating bats	destroy bat homes
chemicals	help farmers

Nouns and Verbs

Listen to the sentences and possible answers. Fill in the bubble for your answer choice.

Example: In this sentence, which word is a noun?

The lazy cat looked out the window.

Ⓐ lazy
Ⓑ cat
Ⓒ looked
Ⓓ out

1. In this sentence, which word is a noun?

The furry bats at the zoo hang from a ledge.

Ⓐ hang
Ⓑ bats
Ⓒ furry
Ⓓ from

2. In this sentence, which word is a noun?

The sun was hot on my face.

Ⓐ was
Ⓑ my
Ⓒ hot
Ⓓ sun

3. In this sentence, which word is a noun?

The full moon shines brightly on the lake.

Ⓐ full
Ⓑ brightly
Ⓒ moon
Ⓓ shines

4. In this sentence, which word is a noun?

The old couch had a loose spring.

Ⓐ old
Ⓑ loose
Ⓒ had
Ⓓ couch

5. In this sentence, which word is a verb?

My friends came late on Saturday.

Ⓐ friends
Ⓑ came
Ⓒ late
Ⓓ Saturday

6. In this sentence, which word is a verb?

The piano player hit the wrong note.

Ⓐ hit
Ⓑ player
Ⓒ wrong
Ⓓ piano

7. In this sentence, which word is a verb?

The pitcher always catches the fly balls.

Ⓐ always
Ⓑ catches
Ⓒ balls
Ⓓ pitcher

8. In this sentence, which word is a verb?

Toby carefully painted his model airplane.

Ⓐ model
Ⓑ carefully
Ⓒ painted
Ⓓ airplane

Main Idea and Key Details

Listen to the question and possible answers. Fill in the bubble for your answer choice.

Example: Which sentence tells the main idea?

- Ⓐ My baby sister laughs loudly when I play with her.
- Ⓑ Babies make a lot of noise.
- Ⓒ We could hear the baby in the stroller crying.
- Ⓓ When the baby is in his crib, he talks aloud to himself.

1. Which sentence tells the main idea?

- Ⓐ The dog next door barks when people walk by.
- Ⓑ He barks when cars drive by.
- Ⓒ Sometimes it's hard to think because of all that barking.
- Ⓓ The dog next door is always barking.

2. Which sentence tells the main idea?

- Ⓐ It's hard to get up in the morning.
- Ⓑ When the alarm clock rings, sometimes I go back to sleep.
- Ⓒ My blankets are warm and I don't like the cold morning air.
- Ⓓ I hate to leave my dreams behind.

3. Which sentence tells the main idea?

- Ⓐ Every time we get to choose what's for dinner, Elvin wants pizza.
- Ⓑ Pizza is Elvin's favorite food.
- Ⓒ Elvin asks Mom to always keep pizza in the freezer.
- Ⓓ Elvin argues with me if I want macaroni instead of pizza.

4. Which sentence tells the main idea?

- Ⓐ At school, kids admired my new shoes.
- Ⓑ Mom said she thought the red shoe looked the best on me.
- Ⓒ Even my older sister complimented me on my shoes.
- Ⓓ Everybody likes my new red shoes.

5. Which sentence tells the main idea?

- Ⓐ The baby birds cheep loudly when their mother brings worms.
- Ⓑ The baby birds cheep when their father leaves the nest.
- Ⓒ Baby birds make a lot of noise.
- Ⓓ The baby birds cheep early in the morning.

Let's Focus: "Africa Digs"

Content Focus
digging in Africa

Type of Text
informational

Big Ideas
Consider the following Big Idea questions. Write your answer for each question.

What can we learn from fossils?

____

____

Why is it hard to recover fossils?

____

____

Work with your teacher to follow these instructions using the map.

- Place an X to mark where you live.
- Mark a C on Chicago.
- Label the Atlantic Ocean.

Reading for a Purpose

1. Who led the dig in Niger, Africa?
2. Why did Dr. Sereno need help from the Touareg tribe?
3. How did the dig team protect the fossils?
4. How did the dig team load the bones onto trucks?
5. How did the scientists clean the bones?
6. Why did Dr. Sereno's team make bones?
7. What did the team create to help build the skeleton?
8. How did they make the casts look like real fossils?

Key Passage Vocabulary: "Africa Digs"

Rate your knowledge of the words. Define the words. Draw a picture to help you remember the definition.

Vocabulary	Knowledge Rating	Definition	Picture
desert	0 1 2 3		
emerge	0 1 2 3		
pulley	0 1 2 3		
port	0 1 2 3		
precise	0 1 2 3		
create	0 1 2 3		
fragile	0 1 2 3		
display	0 1 2 3		

Africa Digs

Dr. Paul Sereno digs dinosaur bones. He gets a thrill when he digs up the bones of dinosaurs that lived millions of years ago. In 1997, Dr. Sereno led a dig in Niger, Africa. He took 18 scientists with him. 5 The Touareg tribe helped his team look for bones. The Touareg people live in Niger. They know their **desert** land best. They know where to look for bones.

desert
dry place with few plants

The dig was a success. Dr. Sereno's team had a fantastic find. They found a new dinosaur. The 10 Touareg told them a legend about a very big animal. They call it *Jobar.* The Touareg showed them where to look for the bones. The scientists named the dinosaur *Jobaria.* It means "giant." How did they dig up the *Jobaria?* Dr. Sereno followed 10 steps to dig up *Jobaria.*

Step 1: We've Got Some!

15 The Touareg lead the team to a special place. Bones stick out of desert rock. The Touareg tell the scientists their legend. These bones belong to the giant beast, *Jobar.*

Step 2: Digging In

20 The dig begins. They use hammers, chisels, and drills. They work for 10 weeks. A huge skeleton **emerges**. It has been buried for 135 million years! Fifteen tons of rock cover it. The team carefully takes 25 the bones from the rock.

emerge
to come out of or appear

The Touareg tribe helped the team.

Step 3: Wrap It Up

They have to make "jackets" to protect the fossils. They cover the bones with paper or foil. They cut burlap strips and dip them in plaster. They wrap each bone with the burlap strips. First, they cover one side. 30 The strip dries into a hard jacket. Then, they cover the other side. They number the jackets. They log each number in the dig's log.

Step 4: Move It Out

The team must take the bones to their lab in Chicago. Twenty tons of bones have to be moved. Some 35 weigh more than 500 pounds. There is no easy way to move them. They use a tripod, **pulleys**, rope, and a chain. They load the bones onto trucks. They drive 1,000 miles to a **port** in Ghana. They put the bones on a ship, which takes them across the Atlantic. Then, the 40 bones are shipped to Chicago.

pulley
small wheel over which a rope moves to help lift or move objects

port
a place on the water where people load and unload ships

Step 5: Unwrap It

The team carefully opens each piece and cleans each bone. They match the numbers on the jackets to 45 the numbers in the dig's log. The bones are put in the right order. Now it's time to rebuild the skeleton.

Step 6: Clean 'Em Up

This step takes two 50 years and hundreds of hours. They use dental tools, tiny jackhammers, and chemicals. The work is careful and **precise**. 55 They have to clean more than 200 bones. These bones came from the adult *Jobaria*. But they have some other bones as well. These 60 are from young *Jobaria*. They clean these bones too.

precise
exact or pays attention to details

Dr. Paul Sereno and his team at the African dig site

Dr. Paul Sereno examines the dinosaur bones.

Step 7: And the Missing Pieces?

They have good luck! They have almost all of the adult's bones. What about the ones that are missing? They fill in the missing bones by making them out of
65 foam and clay.

Step 8: Make a Plan

All of the bones are clean. The missing bones are made. At last, they can make a model. From it, they **create** a blueprint. This is the plan to rebuild the skeleton. First, they lay out the tail bones. They place
70 them in order. Next, they study how to put the bones back together. Now, they can see the huge size of the dinosaur.

create
to make

fragile
easily broken or delicate

display
to show or put something in a place where others can see it

Step 9: Copy the Fossils

Jobaria's bones are too heavy and **fragile** to put together. Dr. Sereno's team wants to **display** 75 the dinosaur. What can they do? They copy the skeleton. They make molds. They create copies of the bones.

Step 10: Stack It Up

They attach the casts of the bones to a steel frame. The hard steel frame 80 is covered by the bones.

Finally: Share the Discovery!

They paint the casts to look like the real fossils. They are white with tints of green and red. These colors come from copper and iron in the 85 soil. At last, they pose the dinosaur. It looks so real! You can almost hear that dinosaur roar!

Adapted with permission from
"Finding the Pieces...
and Putting Them Back Together Again"
by Michelle Laliberte

Did You Know?

The ancient Greeks did not know about dinosaurs. But they had a word, *deinos,* that meant "terrible" or "monstrous" and a word, *saur,* that meant "lizard." In the 1800s when scientists began to study fossilized bones of these beasts, they used the Greek words to name them and gave us the word *dinosaur.*

Why is "terrible lizard" a good name for these animals?

Multiple-Meaning Map

Determine the meanings of the word *dig.* Write the definitions in the boxes. Use the word in a sentence on the lines below the boxes.

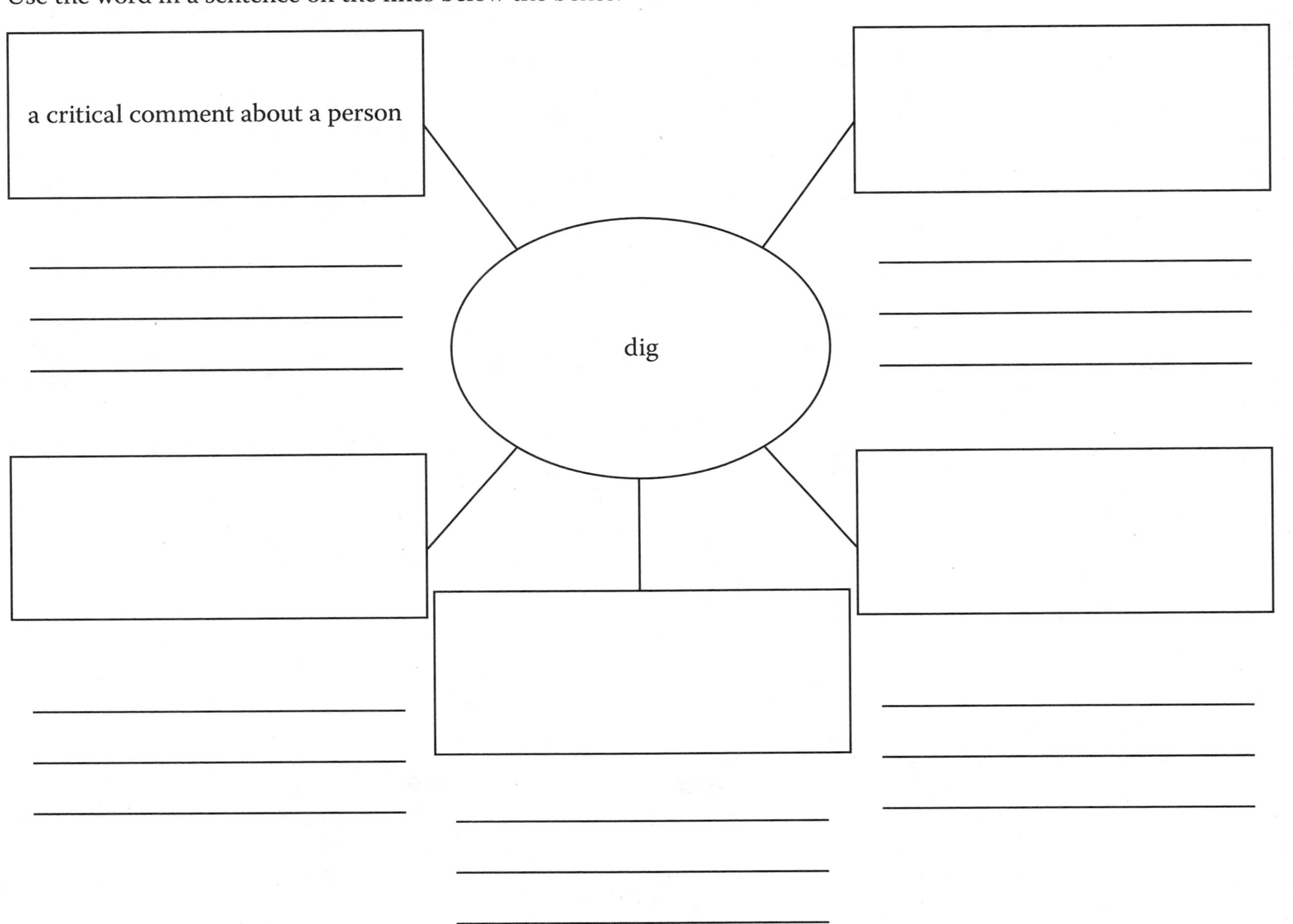

Multiple-Meaning Map

Determine the meanings of the word *log*. Write the definitions in the boxes. Use the word in a sentence on the lines below the boxes.

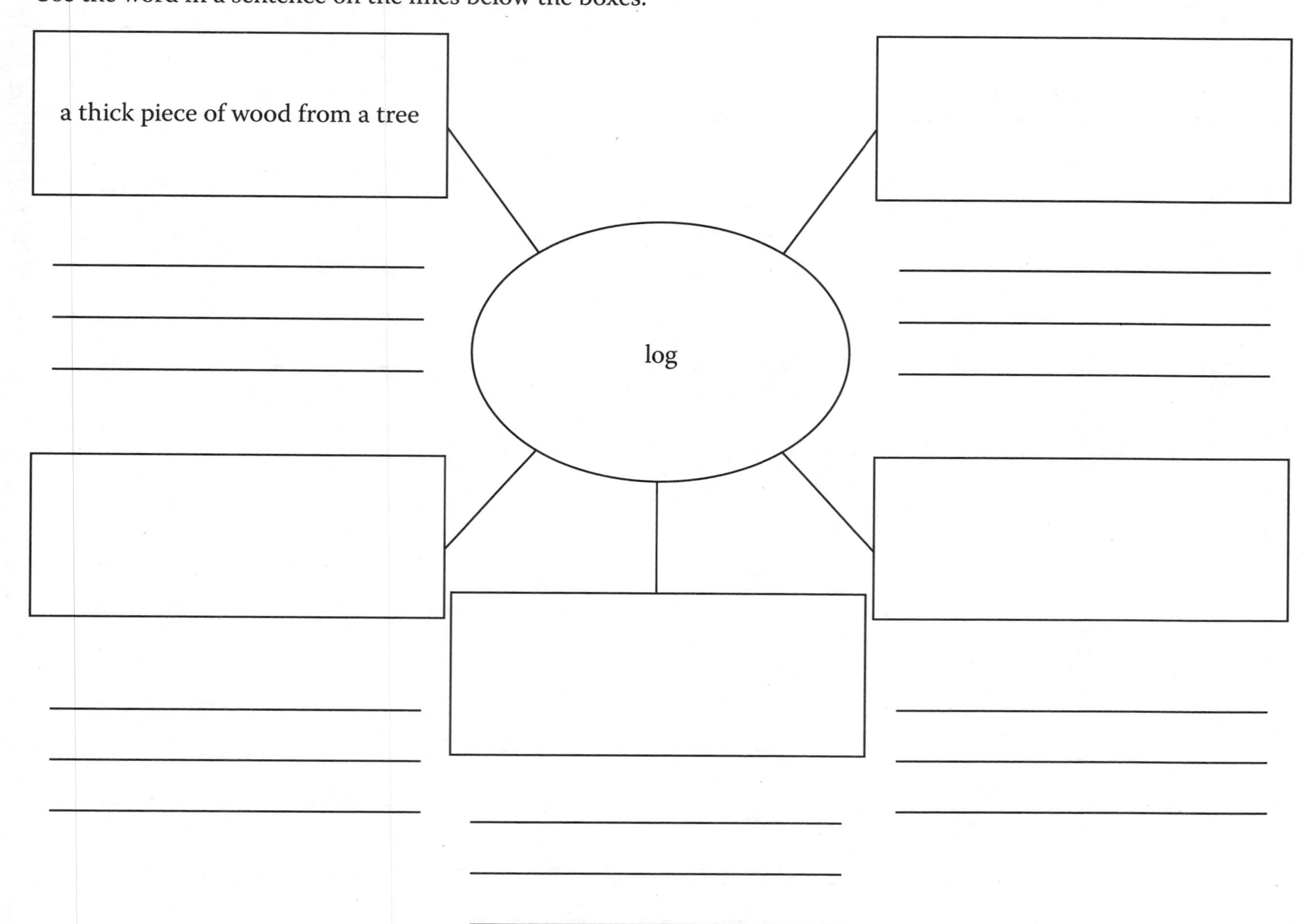

Find It: Plural Nouns

Part A

Read the sentences. Underline the plural nouns in each sentence.

1. He took 18 scientists with him.
2. They knew where to look for bones.
3. They use hammers, chisels, and drills.
4. They have to make jackets to protect the fossils.
5. They wrap the bones with the burlap strips.

Part B

Sort the plural nouns according to the question they answer: *who* or *what.*

Who	What

Part C

Rewrite each plural noun from the sentences in Part A as a singular noun.

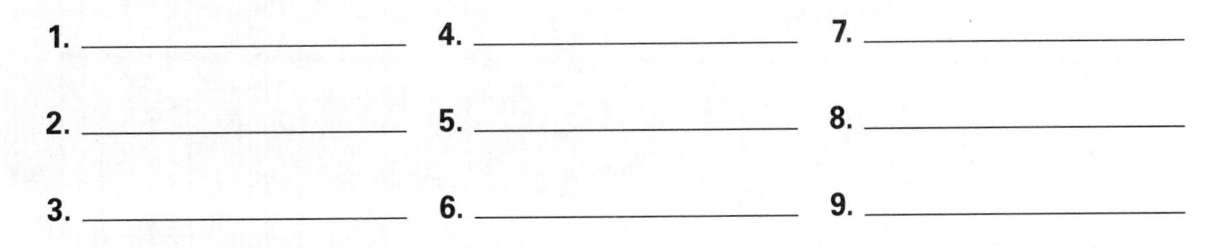

1. ____________ 4. ____________ 7. ____________

2. ____________ 5. ____________ 8. ____________

3. ____________ 6. ____________ 9. ____________

Parts of a Sentence

Part A

Read each group of words. Place a check mark by the questions that can be answered. Identify the group of words by checking Phrase or Sentence.

	Who or What?	Did what?	Phrase	Sentence
1. mac sat in the fast cab				
2. the fast ram				
3. the man ran to the lab				
4. plans a nap				
5. taps the fan				

Part B

Correct the sentences in the paragraph. Insert missing end marks. Draw three lines underneath the first letter of a word that needs to be capitalized.

bats help bats eat insects insects bite people and pets too

many insects kill crops many farmers would lose their

farms people would not have food bats help get rid of

insects

Word Fluency

Read the words fluently.

	Correct	Errors
1st Try		
2nd Try		

yams	sick	back	gut	pass	wax	jam	mud	vans	luck	10
back	gut	pass	wax	jam	mud	vans	luck	fix	but	20
pass	wax	jam	mud	vans	luck	fix	but	zip	cuts	30
jam	mud	vans	luck	fix	but	zip	cuts	miss	fuss	40
vans	luck	fix	but	zip	cuts	miss	fuss	will	rugs	50
fix	but	zip	cuts	miss	fuss	will	rugs	kicks	hut	60
zip	cuts	miss	fuss	will	rugs	kicks	hut	sick	yams	70
miss	fuss	will	rugs	kicks	hut	sick	yams	gut	back	80
will	rugs	kicks	hut	sick	yams	gut	back	wax	pass	90
kicks	hut	sick	yams	gut	back	wax	pass	mud	jam	100

Antonyms

Listen to the word. Choose the antonym from the word bank and write it on the line.

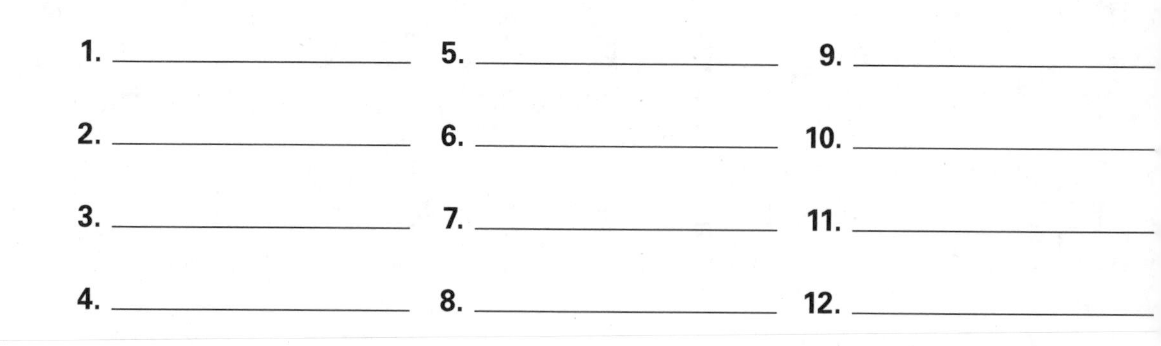

Word Bank

fat	sad	full	up	big	pull
win	back	sun	sick	flat	bad

Noun Forms

Singular Noun

Singular means "one of something."

Plural Noun

Adding *-s* changes a singular noun to a plural noun.

Adding the ending *-s* to a singular noun	makes a plural noun.
■ map + s = maps	■ I had the **maps** in my bag.
■ dig + s = digs	■ The **digs** were fun.
■ cat + s = cats	■ The **cats** sat on the mats.

Singular Possessive Noun

Adding *-'s* to a noun shows possession.

Adding the ending *-'s* to a singular noun	makes a possessive singular noun.
■ Stan + 's = Stan's	■ **Stan's** maps are at camp.
■ dig + 's = dig's	■ The **dig's** logbook is full.
■ man + 's = man's	■ The **man's** cap is black.

The Owner: Singular Possessive Nouns

Part A

Read the sentences. Fill in the blanks to show the meaning of the *-'s* in each sentence.

1. The **man's map** means the ______________ that belongs to the ______________.

2. **Ann's pan** means a ______________ owned by ______________.

3. The **cab's** red **mat** means one ______________ that belongs in the ______________.

4. **Sam's plant** means a ______________ that belongs to ______________.

Part B

Read the sentences. Underline each possessive noun. Draw an arrow to show what the noun owns or possesses.

1. The man's hat is on the cat.

2. Ann's big boat is at the port near town.

3. They found bones at Paul's dig.

4. Paul used clay to create the dinosaur's missing bones.

5. I have Stan's tools and Pat's paint.

6. Paul writes in the dig's logbook at camp.

7. The desert's land is dry.

8. They search Niger's desert for *Jobaria*'s bones.

9. The team's work is precise.

10. The pulley's rope connects to the bones.

Answering *How* and *Why* Questions

Read the passage. Use the information to answer the questions.

Boston's Big Dig

Traffic is a big problem in cities. Millions of people use the roads to get to work and school. Municipal and city governments have the responsibility to maintain bridges, roads, and tunnels; but, as time passes, all structures suffer wear and tear. Sometimes, *everything* needs fixing. In Boston, Massachusetts, that is what happened. Road congestion in Boston was so fierce in the 1990s that for up to 10 hours of the day, traffic could only crawl. The city had a high accident rate, combined with heavy noise and air pollution. The metropolitan area needed new bridges, roads, and tunnels. The solution to the problem was to replace roads with a huge underground tunnel.

1. Why is traffic a problem in big cities? ______________________________

____

____

2. Why do bridges, roads, and tunnels need fixing? ______________________________

____

____

3. Why was it even worse in Boston? ______________________________

____

____

4. Most of the time, how did traffic move? ______________________________

____

____

5. How did Boston solve its traffic problem? ______________________________

____

____

Phrase Fluency

Read each phrase fluently.

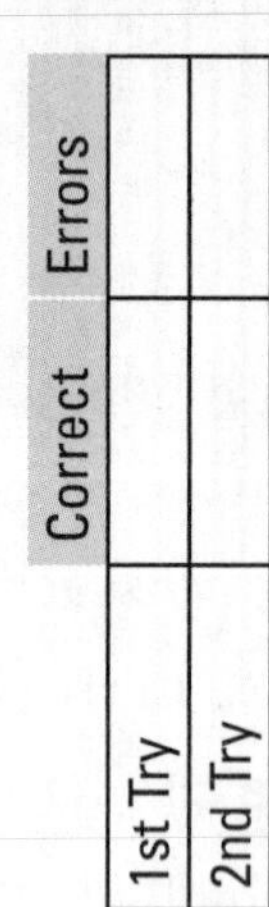

Bill and Vick	3	in a big bag	83
fill the bill	6	Rick's pals	85
cans in the sacks	10	the fizz in the cup	90
fill the back	13	of the van	93
Sam's sack	15	give him a mat	97
has a sax	18	Kip's big sick fox	101
can the man	21	the six kids in the wigs	107
the fax in the bin	26	fix the van	110
pick jazz	28	six big wigs	113
pits in the pan	32	rip the sacks and bags	118
in the big sack	36	kids win	120
Nick's bills	38	zip the bags	123
the mad lads	41	into the box	126
the kids in the tan hats	47	the ruts on the hill	131
pick the hits	50	the pig's mud	134
kick the puck	53	fans in the cab	138
Zack's fax	55	tip the pan	141
Jack's bull	57	pack the sack	144
wax on the lid	61	give the hams and hats	149
is a kick	64	the duck's bill	152
the big gull	67	have Jack and Sam	156
give a tip	70	have his back	159
jazz on the sax	74	has a big rip	163
Vick's lip	76	pick one kid	166
the van's rims	79	my six sacks	169

Singular Possessives and Plural Nouns

Part A

Read the phrases. Circle all of the nouns in each phrase. Decide whether each noun is a singular noun, plural noun, or singular possessive noun. Write each noun in the appropriate column.

1. Rick's pals
2. cans in the sacks
3. fill the bill
4. the six kids in the wigs
5. fix the van
6. Sam's sack

Nouns		
Singular	**Plural**	**Singular Possessive**

Part B

Read the sentence frames. Circle the word that correctly completes each sentence. Write the word on the line. Read the sentence again.

1. The raft is at ________________ camp.
   Stans or Stan's

2. ________________ logbook is at her camp by the dig.
   Anns or Ann's

3. Fran has ________________ in her bag.
   hats or hat's

4. ________________ plans are good.
   Sams or Sam's

5. The man's ________________ sat on his tools.
   cats or cat's

Sentence Morphs

Read the phrases. Scoop them in the complete sentences.

He has a bag of rags in the cab He has a bag of rags in the cab.	The man will tag the bag for the win The man will tag the bag for the win.	The tan wig on the rack is for Jan The tan wig on the rack is for Jan.
Will has a fat tick on his back Will has a fat tick on his back.	Jack and Jill live by the dam Jack and Jill live by the dam.	Give Zack the bibs and mats for the kids Give Zack the bibs and mats for the kids.
The lid of the bin has a rat on it The lid of the bin has a rat on it.	Fill the bun and pack it in the bag Fill the bun and pack it in the bag.	Max hid the bag of yams for his pal Max hid the bag of yams for his pal.

Generating Questions: *How* and *Why*

Look at the following pictures. Write a *how* question on the first pair of lines. Write a *why* question on the second pair of lines. Use all of the clues in the picture and be creative.

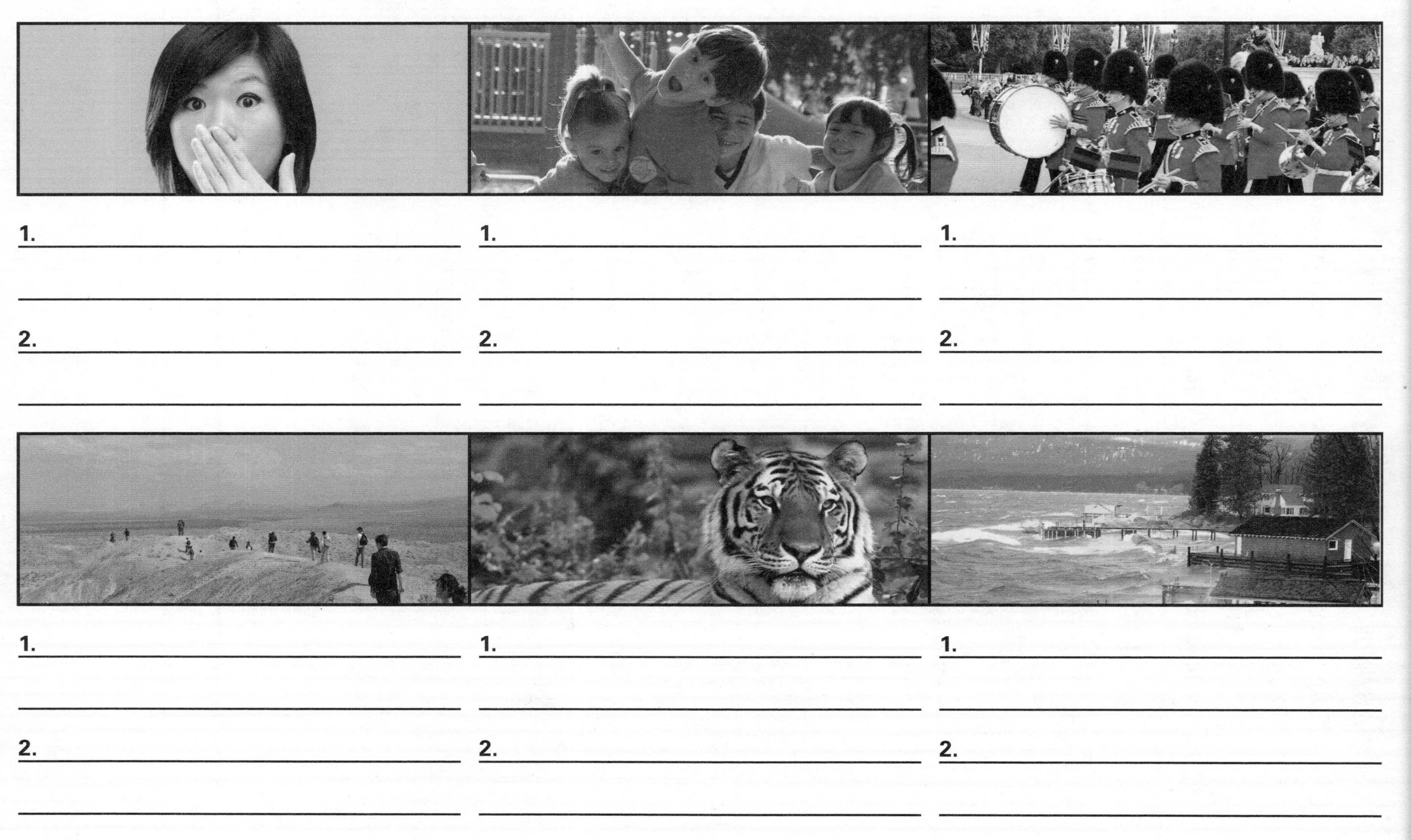

1. ______________________

2. ______________________

1. ______________________

2. ______________________

1. ______________________

2. ______________________

1. ______________________

2. ______________________

1. ______________________

2. ______________________

1. ______________________

2. ______________________

Define It

Determine the category and attributes of each word. Then, write the definition.

Word		Category		Attribute(s)
legend	=	story	+	takes place long ago; can't be proven

Definition:
A legend is a story from long ago that is thought to be true but that can't be proven.

Word		Category		Attribute(s)
scientist	=		+	

Definition:

Word		Category		Attribute(s)
dinosaur	=		+	

Definition:

Word		Category		Attribute(s)
tint	=		+	

Definition:

Close Reading: Guided Highlighting

Read the text and complete the tasks.

Africa Digs

Dr. Paul Sereno digs dinosaur bones. He gets a thrill when he digs up the bones of dinosaurs that lived millions of years ago. In 1997, Dr. Sereno led a dig in Niger, Africa. He took 18 scientists with him. The Touareg tribe helped his team look for bones. The Touareg people live in Niger. They 5 know their **desert** land best. They know where to look for bones.

The dig was a success. Dr. Sereno's team had a fantastic find. They found a new dinosaur. The Touareg told them a legend about a very big animal. They call it *Jobar.* The Touareg showed them where to look for the bones. The scientists named the dinosaur *Jobaria.* It means "giant." How did they 10 dig up the *Jobaria?* Dr. Sereno followed 10 steps to dig up *Jobaria.*

- **What will the rest of the passage be about? Write a topic sentence.**

____

____

Step 1: We've Got Some!

The Touareg lead the team to a special place. Bones stick out of desert rock. The Touareg tell the scientists their legend. These bones belong to the giant beast, *Jobar.*

Step 2: Digging In

The dig begins. They use hammers, chisels, and drills. They work for 15 10 weeks. A huge skeleton **emerges**. It has been buried for 135 million years! Fifteen tons of rock cover it. The team carefully takes the bones from the rock.

Step 3: Wrap It Up

They have to make "jackets" to protect the fossils. They cover the bones with paper or foil. They cut burlap strips and dip them in plaster. They 20 wrap each bone with the burlap strips. First, they cover one side. The strip dries into a hard jacket. Then, they cover the other side. They number the jackets. They log each number in the dig's log.

Close Reading: Guided Highlighting (*cont.*)

Step 4: Move It Out

The team must take the bones to their lab in Chicago. Twenty tons of bones have to be moved. Some weigh more than 500 pounds. There is no 25 easy way to move them. They use a tripod, **pulleys**, rope, and a chain. They load the bones onto trucks. They drive 1,000 miles to a **port** in Ghana. They put the bones on a ship, which takes them across the Atlantic. Then, the bones are shipped to Chicago.

- **What is the section mostly about? Fill in the blanks to complete the sentences.** Without machines, 20 tons of bones need to be moved from ____________________, across the ____________________ Ocean by ____________________. Next, the bones are shipped across land to ____________________.

Step 5: Unwrap It

The team carefully opens each piece and cleans each bone. They match the 30 numbers on the jackets to the numbers in the dig's log. The bones are put in the right order. Now it's time to rebuild the skeleton.

- **Read the IVF summary sentence for this section.** Step 5: Unwrap It describes how the team prepares the bones before rebuilding the skeleton.

Step 6: Clean 'Em Up

This step takes two years and hundreds of hours. They use dental tools, tiny jackhammers, and chemicals. The work is careful and **precise**. They have to clean more than 200 bones. These bones came from the adult 35 *Jobaria*. But they have some other bones as well. These are from young *Jobaria*. They clean these bones too.

- **Finish the IVF summary sentence for this section. Use the word *precise* in your sentence.**

  Step 6: Clean 'Em Up explains how ______________________________

  ____

  ____.

Close Reading: Guided Highlighting (*cont.*)

Step 7: And the Missing Pieces?
They have good luck! They have almost all of the adult's bones. What about the ones that are missing? They fill in the missing bones by making them out of foam and clay.

- **Complete the sentence frame to write an IVF summary sentence for this section. Identify the Item. Select a Verb. Finish your thought.**

  Step 7: And the Missing Pieces? tells how ____________________

  ____

  ____________________.

Step 8: Make a Plan
40 All of the bones are clean. The missing bones are made. At last, they can make a model. From it, they **create** a blueprint. This is the plan to rebuild the skeleton. First, they lay out the tail bones. They place them in order. Next, they study how to put the bones back together. Now, they can see the huge size of the dinosaur.

Step 9: Copy the Fossils
45 *Jobaria*'s bones are too heavy and **fragile** to put together. Dr. Sereno's team wants to **display** the dinosaur. What can they do? They copy the skeleton. They make molds. They create copies of the bones.

Step 10: Stack It Up
They attach the casts of the bones to a steel frame. The hard steel frame is covered by the bones.

Finally: Share the Discovery!
50 They paint the casts to look like the real fossils. They are white with tints of green and red. These colors come from copper and iron in the soil. At last, they pose the dinosaur. It looks so real! You can almost hear that dinosaur roar!

Masterpiece Sentences: Stages 1 and 2

Use the information in the chart to build four sentences. Remember to use capital letters and punctuation marks for each sentence.

Subject	Predicate	Direct Object
Who or What did it?	**What did they do?**	**What did they do it to?**
scientists	tagged	the bones
the dig team	cleaned	the fossils
Dr. Sereno	led	the dig
the fabric strips	protected	each bone

1. ______________________________

2. ______________________________

3. ______________________________

4. ______________________________

Ask and Answer Questions

Reread "Africa Digs." After each section, write a question for your partner to answer using question words that you have learned so far. Try not to use the same question word twice. Be prepared to answer your question orally. Use the Question Words chart on page 14 to help you.

Introduction *Who?* *Where?*

1. ____

Step 1: We've Got Some! and Step 2: Digging In *What?* *When?*

2. ____

Step 3: Wrap It Up and Step 4: Move It Out *Where?* *Is/Are?*

3. ____

Step 5: Unwrap It and Step 6: Clean 'Em Up *What?* *How?*

4. ____

Step 7: And the Missing Pieces? and
Step 8: Make a Plan *How?* *Why?*

5. ____

Lines 73–87: *What?* *Why?*

6. ____

Passage Comprehension

Underline the question word in each question. Then, answer each question using a complete sentence. Write the evidence from the text.

1. Who led the dig in Niger, Africa?

   ____

   Text Evidence: ______________________________

2. Why did Dr. Sereno need help from the Touareg tribe?

   ____

   ____

   Text Evidence: ______________________________

   ____

3. How did the dig team protect the fossils?

   ____

   ____

   Text Evidence: ______________________________

   ____

   ____

   ____

4. How did the dig team load the bones onto trucks?

   ____

   ____

   Text Evidence: ______________________________

   ____

5. How did the scientists clean the bones?

   ____

   ____

   Text Evidence: ______________________________

   ____

   ____

Passage Comprehension (*cont.*)

6. Why did Dr. Sereno's team make bones?

____

Text Evidence: ____

____

7. What did the team create to help them build the skeleton?

____

____

Text Evidence: ____

____

8. How did they make the casts look like real fossils?

____

____

____

Text Evidence: ____

____

____

Four-Square

Write the definition of *fragile*. Then, write examples and antonyms of the word in the appropriate boxes.

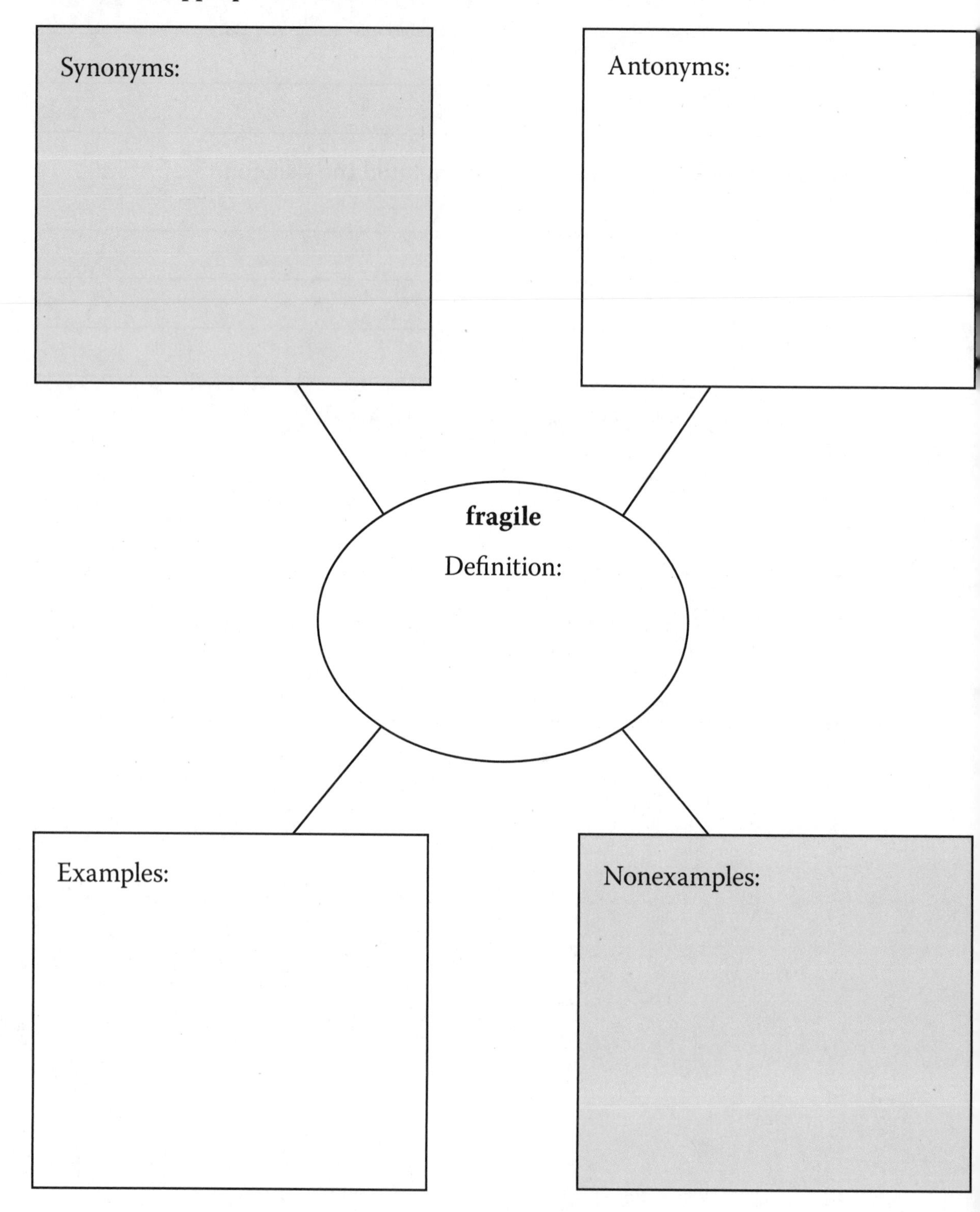

Making Connections

Make connections to the word *scientist* by generating other words related to the word.

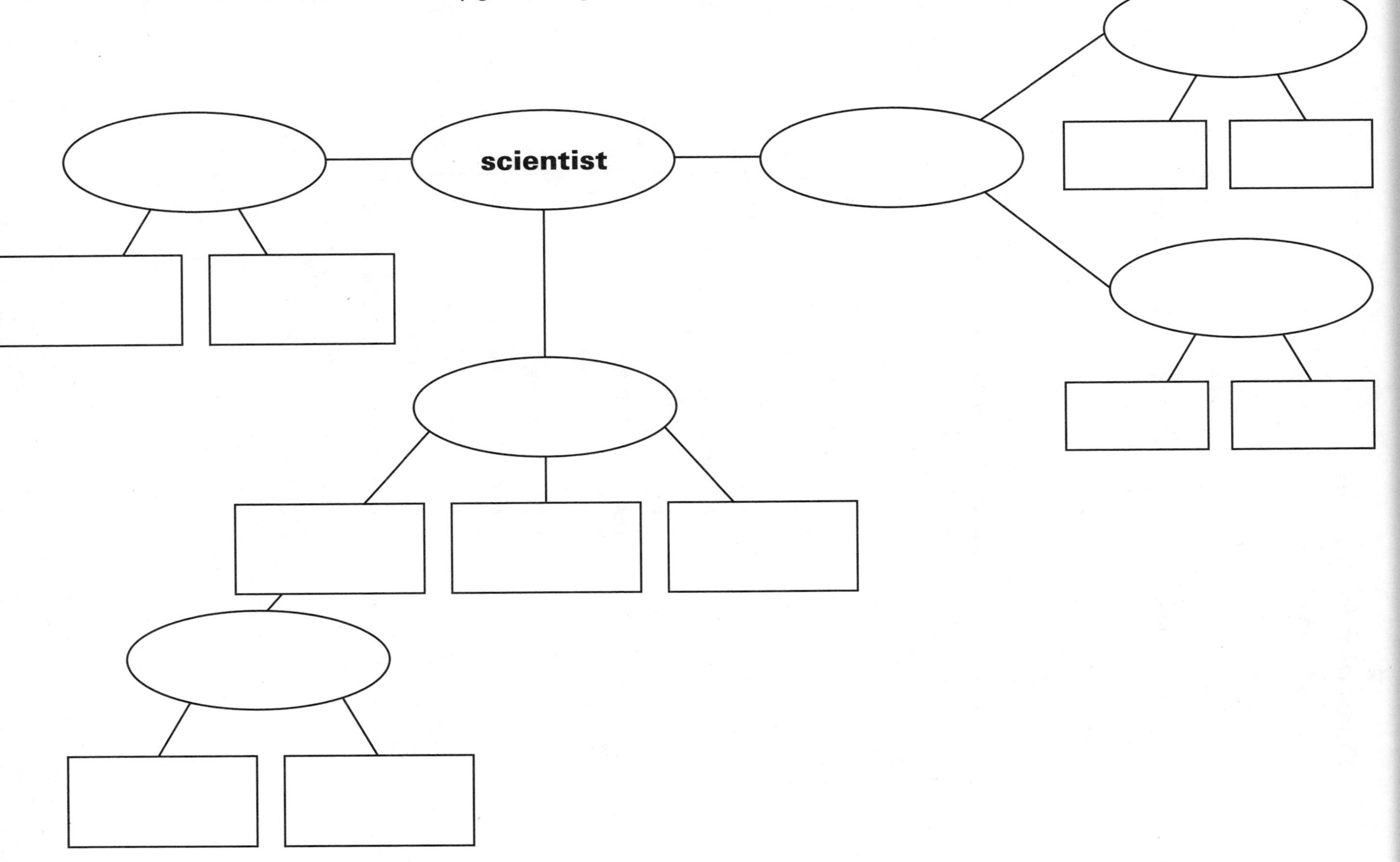

Parts of a Paragraph

Topic sentence tells what the paragraph is about.

Supporting details give facts or reasons about the topic.

Transition words link one supporting detail to the next.

Elaborations add interest for the reader. **Elaborations (Es)** are **e**xplanations, **e**xamples, and **e**vidence.

Conclusion restates the topic sentence or big idea.

Read the paragraph. Highlight the parts of the paragraph. The topic sentence is green. Supporting details and transition words are yellow. The elaborations are pink, and the conclusion is green. Circle the transition words, and label each part of the paragraph.

The Benefits of Exercise

Regular exercise benefits people's health in two important ways. One benefit is that exercise improves people's physical health. It makes the heart, lungs, bones, and muscles stronger and keeps people at a healthy weight. Exercise is also good for the mind. It makes people feel better about themselves and calms them down when they are angry or stressed. When people regularly do physical activities they enjoy, their bodies and minds stay fit, happy, and healthy.

Identify Parts of a Paragraph

Read the paragraph. Highlight the topic sentence green. Highlight the supporting details yellow. Highlight elaborations pink. Circle the transitions, and label the parts of the paragraph.

Millions of years ago, two kinds of giant animals lived in the area that is now Northern Africa. One animal was a dinosaur known as *Jobaria*. This dinosaur was huge. It probably looked terrifying to other animals, but it ate only plants. The other giant animal was a huge crocodile. Scientists named the animal SuperCroc. SuperCroc weighed about as much as an elephant and grew as long as 40 feet. That's about as long as a city bus! Today, bones of both dinosaurs are on display for the whole world to see.

Blueprint for Writing + Parts of a Paragraph

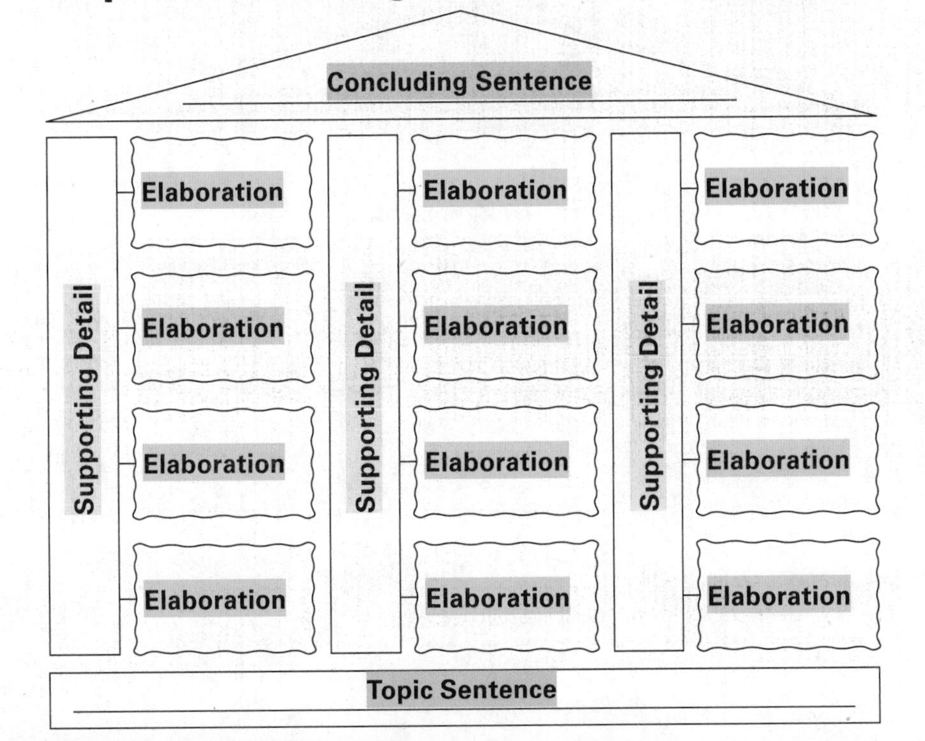

Word Fluency

Read the words fluently.

	Correct	Errors
1st Try		
2nd Try		

yams	sick	back	gut	pass	wax	jam	mud	vans	luck	10
back	gut	pass	wax	jam	mud	vans	luck	fix	but	20
pass	wax	jam	mud	vans	luck	fix	but	zip	cuts	30
jam	mud	vans	luck	fix	but	zip	cuts	miss	fuss	40
vans	luck	fix	but	zip	cuts	miss	fuss	will	rugs	50
fix	but	zip	cuts	miss	fuss	will	rugs	kicks	hut	60
zip	cuts	miss	fuss	will	rugs	kicks	hut	sick	yams	70
miss	fuss	will	rugs	kicks	hut	sick	yams	gut	back	80
will	rugs	kicks	hut	sick	yams	gut	back	wax	pass	90
kicks	hut	sick	yams	gut	back	wax	pass	mud	jam	100

Noun as a Direct Object

A noun can be the direct object—the person, place, or thing that receives the action.

The direct object:

- Is in the predicate part of the sentence
- Answers *What (whom) did they (he, she, it) do it to?*

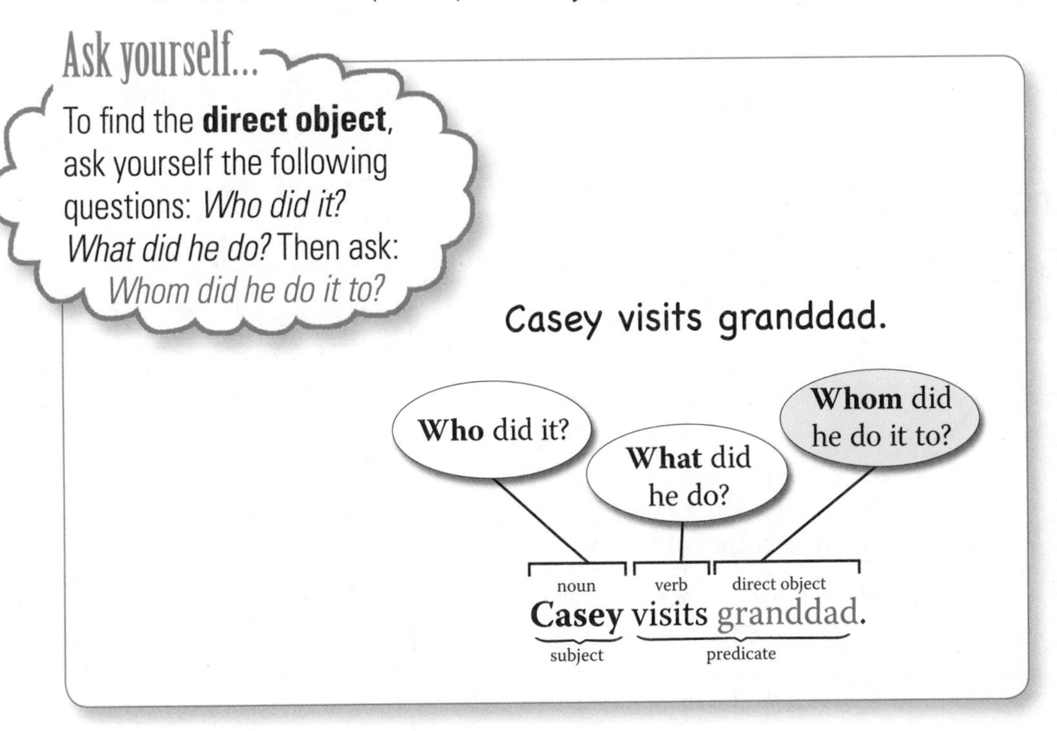

Copy the sentences from class on the lines. Remember to include proper punctuation for each sentence. Underline the direct object in both sentences.

1. ____

____

2. ____

____

Diagramming Subject/Predicate/Direct Object

Write each sentence in the diagram below it. Use the questions to help you fill in the diagram correctly.

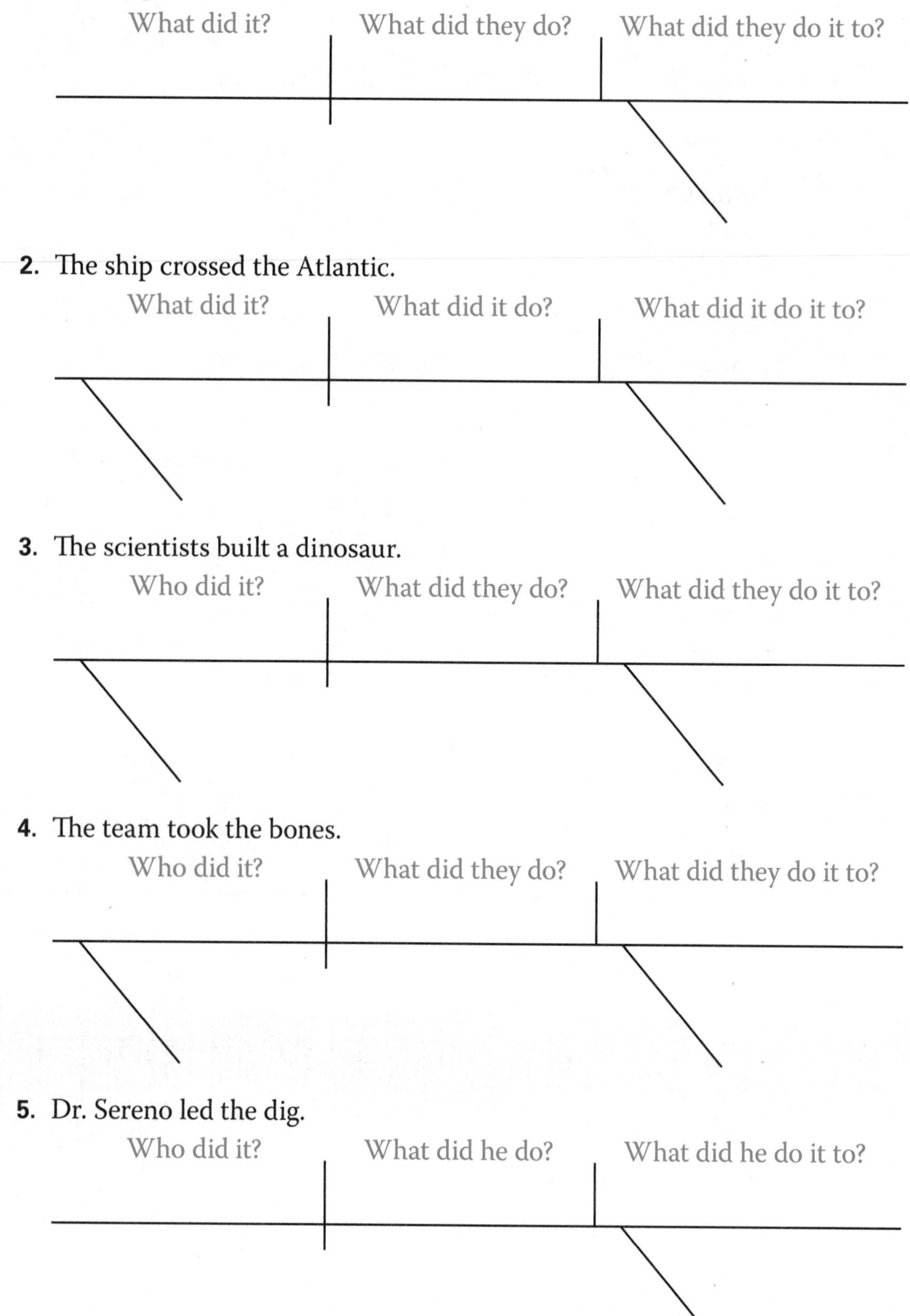

1. Jackets protected the fossils.
2. The ship crossed the Atlantic.
3. The scientists built a dinosaur.
4. The team took the bones.
5. Dr. Sereno led the dig.

Take Note: Writing a Log of Events

Take notes for each step of the dig. Start each note with a strong verb or action word.

Phase 1:

____

____

____

____

____

____

Phase 2:

____

____

____

____

____

____

______________________ **Logbook**

Step 1: ______________________

____

____

Step 2: ______________________

____

Step 3: ______________________

____

Step 4: ______________________

____

Step 5: ______________________

____

Step 6: ______________________

____

Step 7: ______________________

____

Take Note: Writing a Log of Events (*cont.*)

Phase 3:

____

____

____

____

____

____

Logbook

Step 8: ______________________

____

____

Step 9: ______________________

____

Step 10: ______________________

____

Finally, ______________________

____

Number Topic Sentence

Part A

Read each topic sentence and underline the words that tell about the topic. Circle the number word. Answer the questions orally for each topic sentence.

1. Three cities have serious pollution problems.
2. Maps have multiple layers of information.
3. In winter, I watch two high school sports.
4. I enjoy several kinds of music.
5. At our school, the band raises money in three ways.

What is the topic? What will the writer need to tell about the topic?

Part B

Write a number topic sentence using the topic and supporting details provided.

1. Topic: what makes bats unusual

   Supporting Details:
   can fly
   use sonar

   Topic Sentence: ______________________________

   ____

2. Topic: mammals

   Supporting Details:
   warm-blooded
   breathe air
   have hair
   live births

   Topic Sentence: ______________________________

   ____

3. Topic: main phases in the dig for *Jobaria*

   Supporting Details:
   collecting the dinosaur bones
   putting the dinosaur bones together
   displaying the dinosaur bones

   Topic Sentence: ______________________________

   ____

Using New Vocabulary

Fill in the blanks with the appropriate vocabulary words. If you need assistance, use the word bank at the bottom of the page.

There is a legend about a giant beast that used to live in the _______________ in Africa. Scientists went there to dig for the _______________ bones. The scientists needed to be _______________ in where and how they dug. With careful digging, the bones _______________ from the desert. Because they were so heavy, the bones had to be loaded onto trucks using tripods and _______________. The nearest _______________ was 1,000 miles away. After the bones were shipped to Chicago, they were cleaned. They used foam and clay to _______________ the missing pieces. At last, they had a dinosaur to _______________ for everyone to see.

Word Bank

display	port	emerged	pulleys
fragile	desert	create	precise

Plural *-s* and Singular Possessives

Listen to the sentences and possible answers. Fill in the bubble for your answer choice.

Example: Which word in the following sentence is a singular possessive noun?

The boys went over to their friend's house to play video games.

- Ⓐ games
- Ⓑ house
- Ⓒ friend's
- Ⓓ boys

1. Which word in the following sentence is a singular possessive noun?

My dad's car needs new brakes and wipers.

- Ⓐ brakes
- Ⓑ dad's
- Ⓒ wipers
- Ⓓ car

2. Which word in the following sentence is a plural noun?

The team's players were hoping to make one more goal.

- Ⓐ team's
- Ⓑ players
- Ⓒ more
- Ⓓ goal

3. Which word in the following sentence is a singular possessive noun?

The store's window displays were full of funny hats.

- Ⓐ hats
- Ⓑ window
- Ⓒ displays
- Ⓓ store's

4. Which word in the following sentence is a plural noun?

The puppy's toys were all over the floor.

- Ⓐ toys
- Ⓑ all
- Ⓒ puppy's
- Ⓓ floor

5. Which word in the following sentence is a plural noun?

The pet store's kittens are in a box in the window.

- Ⓐ box
- Ⓑ window
- Ⓒ kittens
- Ⓓ store's

Direct Objects

Listen to the sentences and possible answers. Fill in the bubble for your answer choice.

Example: Which word in the following sentence is the direct object?

Peter passed the ball to his friend.

Ⓐ ball
Ⓑ Peter
Ⓒ friend
Ⓓ his

1. Which word in the following sentence is the direct object?

   My sister poured the juice into the glass.

   Ⓐ My
   Ⓑ sister
   Ⓒ juice
   Ⓓ glass

2. Which word in the following sentence is the direct object?

   The man bought our old washer and hauled it off in his truck.

   Ⓐ truck
   Ⓑ man
   Ⓒ it
   Ⓓ washer

3. Which word in the following sentence is the direct object?

   The storm blew the leaves off the trees.

   Ⓐ trees
   Ⓑ leaves
   Ⓒ off
   Ⓓ storm

4. Which word in the following sentence is the direct object?

   I hung my coat on a hook in my room.

   Ⓐ coat
   Ⓑ I
   Ⓒ room
   Ⓓ hook

5. Which word in the following sentence is the direct object?

   We put the cookies in the oven for ten minutes.

   Ⓐ minutes
   Ⓑ cookies
   Ⓒ oven
   Ⓓ We

Antonyms

Listen to the questions and possible answers. Fill in the bubble for your answer choice.

Example: Which word is an antonym for *inside*?

- (A) around
- (B) into
- (C) beside
- (D) outside

1. Which word is an antonym for *full*?
   - (A) stuffed
   - (B) empty
   - (C) ready
   - (D) missing

2. Which word is an antonym for *quiet*?
   - (A) loud
   - (B) silent
   - (C) still
   - (D) afraid

3. Which word is an antonym for *shouting*?
   - (A) whispering
   - (B) talking
   - (C) arguing
   - (D) screaming

4. Which word is an antonym for *sunrise*?
   - (A) noon
   - (B) afternoon
   - (C) sunset
   - (D) night

5. Which word is an antonym for *come*?
   - (A) arrive
   - (B) travel
   - (C) wait
   - (D) go

Let's Focus: "Gemini: The Twins"

Content Focus
constellations

Type of Text
informational

Big Ideas
Consider these Big Idea questions. Write your answer for each question.

Why are constellations important?

____

____

How have various cultures explained the constellation Gemini?

____

____

Informational Preview Checklist: "Gemini: The Twins" on pages 85–87.

- ☐ Title: What clue does it provide about the passage?
- ☐ Pictures and Captions: What additional information is added here?
- ☐ Headings: What topics will this text include?
- ☐ Margin Information: What vocabulary is important to understand this text?
- ☐ Maps, Charts, Graphs: Are additional visuals present that will help me understand?

Reading for a Purpose

1. What is Gemini?
2. How were constellations helpful?
3. Why did the idea of constellations begin?
4. Where can Gemini be seen?
5. What do different cultures say about the Gemini Twins?
6. How were Castor and Pollux alike?
7. What constellation is attacking another constellation in the sky?
8. Is the North Star a constellation? Are the Twins a constellation?

Key Passage Vocabulary: "Gemini: The Twins"

Rate your knowledge of the words. Define the words. Draw a picture to help you remember the definition.

Vocabulary	Knowledge Rating	Definition	Picture
constellation	0 1 2 3		
pattern	0 1 2 3		
ancient	0 1 2 3		
poet	0 1 2 3		
devoted	0 1 2 3		
mortal	0 1 2 3		
expert	0 1 2 3		
brilliant	0 1 2 3		

Gemini: The Twins

Castor

Pollux

On a dark night, turn your eyes up to the sky. The **constellation** Gemini is a sight to see. It has two very bright stars called the Twins. People have known about them for thousands of years. They have been in the sky 5 as long as anyone can remember.

constellation
a group of stars that form a shape

What Are Constellations?

Constellations are fascinating and helpful to many people. They are **patterns** of stars that people see in the sky. These star patterns were invented by people fascinated with the stars. **Ancient poets** of different 10 cultures made up stories about them. Sailors used the stars to navigate across the oceans. Farmers used the stars to tell them when to plant and when to harvest because the same patterns appear in the sky during the same season every year. How long have we been seeing 15 patterns in the night sky? We have done it for at least 6,000 years.

pattern
a picture, image, or design made by repeated items

ancient
very old

poet
a person who writes stories in lines with emotion and rhythm

Why Did the Idea of Constellations Begin?

Constellations are groups of stars with a purpose. Why were star groups made up? There are so many stars! How could we remember them all? We could put 20 them in groups. The groups break the sky into parts. The stars in the sky are divided into 88 constellations. They help us remember which stars are which. How many stars can we see? On a dark night, we see 1,000 to 1,500 stars. Where can we see the Twins? We can 25 see them in the northern hemisphere in November through April. We can see them in the southern hemisphere in December through March.

The Ancient Stories of Gemini

Ancient people invented stories about the Gemini Twins. The Egyptians called them twin plants. The 30 Hindus called them twin gods. Arabs called them twin peacocks. What is the ancient Greek story of Gemini? The Greeks said they were the sons of the Greek god Zeus and the woman Leda. They said that Zeus and Leda had twin sons. Their names were Castor and 35 Pollux. They were **devoted** and loving brothers. They looked alike. But they were not alike. Castor was **mortal** like his mother. He became a horseman. Pollux was immortal like his father. He became a boxer. Both became **expert** soldiers. Castor was killed in battle. 40 Pollux could not bear to be without his twin. Pollux asked his father, Zeus, for help. He asked for Castor to come back to life. Zeus let them be together side by side forever. They are the Twins that shine brightly in the sky. They are the two **brilliant** stars in Gemini.

devoted
loyal; deeply caring

mortal
subject to death; will not live forever

expert
skilled or knowledgeable

brilliant
very bright; giving off lots of light

Look Up

45 When you look up on a dark night, the sky is flooded with star patterns that tell a story.

- Ursa Major (The Great Bear) is identified by the square of the Big Dipper, which forms the bear's body, and a chain of stars, which forms its 50 tail. Ursa Major can be seen in the northern sky throughout the year.
- Ursa Minor (Lesser Bear) is identified by the square of the Little Dipper, which forms the bear's body, and a chain of stars, which forms 55 its tail. Ursa Minor can be seen in the northern sky. The North Star is part of this constellation. This bright star has been helpful to nighttime travelers for centuries.
- Orion (The Hunter) has some of the brightest 60 stars. He is positioned in the sky to fight off a raging bull. Orion stands with his right arm holding a great club uplifted in the air, ready to strike. Over his left arm hangs a lion's skin that he holds up as a shield in front of him to 65 stop the raging bull. Taurus the Mighty Bull is a constellation that is charging right for Orion. Orion is visible throughout the world. We can see this constellation between December and April.
- Leo (The Lion) is one of the easiest constellations 70 to find. An easy way to spot Leo is to look for a backward question mark in the sky, which represents the head and front of the body. In the northern hemisphere, Leo can be located in spring, and in the southern hemisphere it can be 75 located in autumn.
- Centaurus (The Centaur) has the greatest number of visible stars in it. It has 101 stars.
- Hydra (The Water Snake) is the largest constellation. It covers more than 3% of the sky.

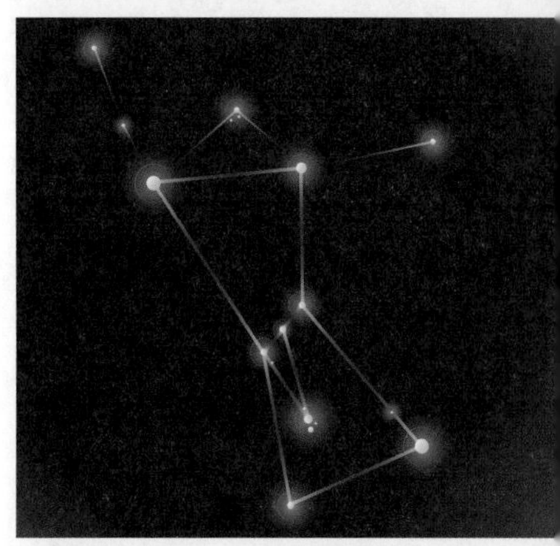

Constellations shown above
TOP: Ursa Major, MIDDLE: Orion, BOTTOM: Leo

Multiple-Meaning Map

Determine the meanings of the word *star.* Write the definitions in the boxes. Use the word in a sentence on the lines below the boxes.

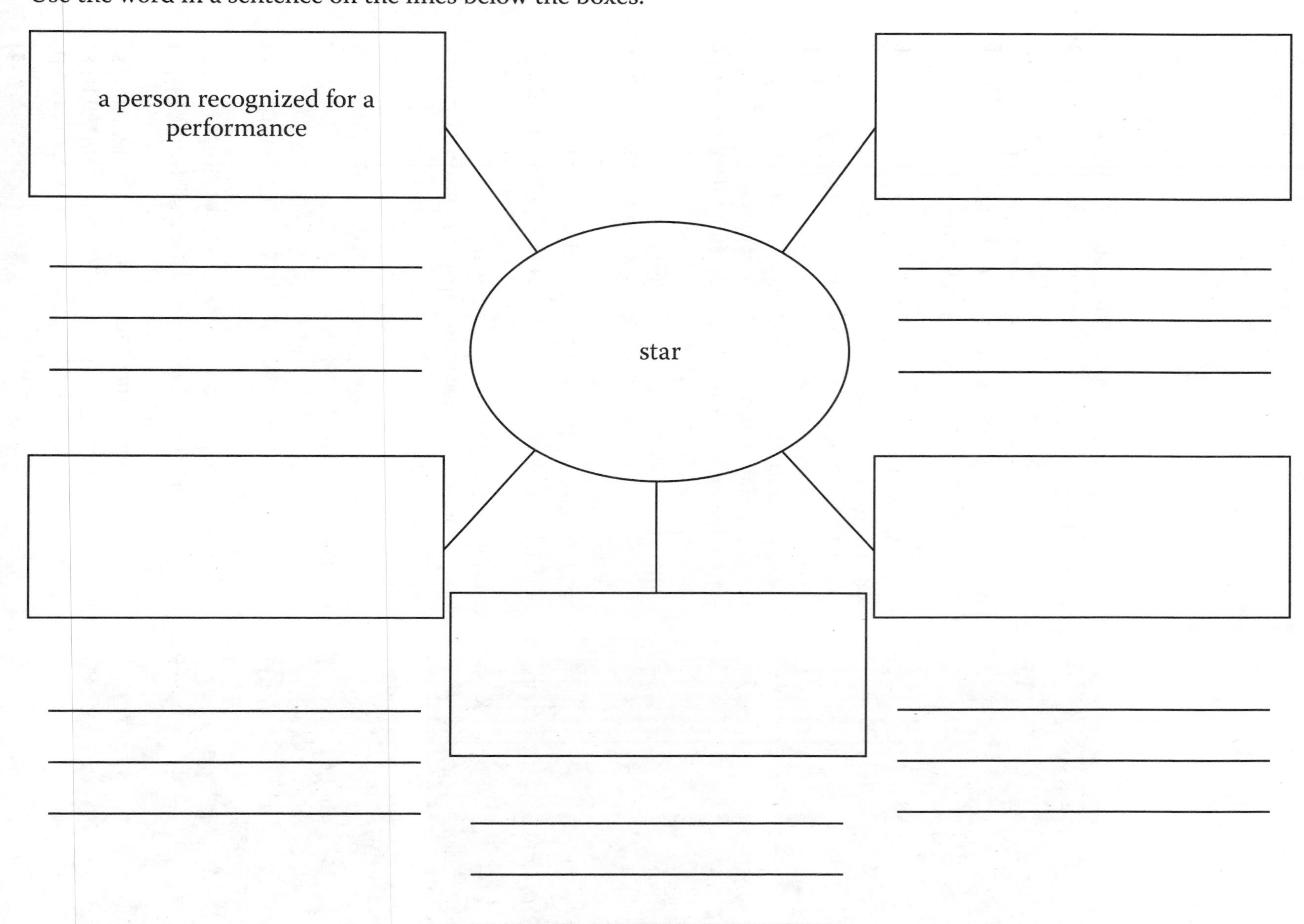

Find It: Prepositions

Read the sentences. Underline the prepositional phrase. Circle the preposition. Write the letter *N* over the nouns in the phrase. Write the prepositions on the bottom line.

1. The Greeks said the stars were the sons of Zeus and Leda.
2. Stories were written by poets.
3. Castor was killed in battle.
4. Pollux wanted Castor by his side.
5. The stars are in the vast sky.
6. They made a map of the stars.
7. In the past, people used the stars.
8. Kim sits by a map.
9. The stars are on the map.
10. The gods lived at home.

Prepositions: ____

Supporting Detail Sentences

Read the topic sentence and detail sentences in each set. Choose two sentences that provide supporting details for that topic sentence. Then write a sentence that could be a third supporting detail.

1. **Topic Sentence:** Breakfast is an important meal for several reasons.

   Possible Supporting Detail Sentences:

   ____ My favorite breakfast is cereal with bananas.

   ____ Dinner is also a very important meal.

   ____ Most people wake up hungry in the morning.

   ____ People's bodies have been working overnight as they were sleeping.

   ____ ____

   ____

2. **Topic Sentence:** Team sports teach kids several helpful lessons.

   Possible Supporting Detail Sentences:

   ____ Kids learn about working together.

   ____ Baseball and soccer are team sports.

   ____ My favorite team sport is football.

   ____ Kids learn that playing is about having fun, not just winning.

   ____ ____

   ____

3. **Topic Sentence:** Smoking causes a number of problems.

   Possible Supporting Detail Sentences:

   ____ I don't like the smell of smoke.

   ____ Smoking pollutes the air for others to breathe.

   ____ Smoking can be a fire hazard.

   ____ People cannot smoke in most restaurants.

   ____ ____

   ____

IVF Topic Sentences

Fill in the missing elements in the IVF topic sentences below. Use the verb bank to choose a different verb for each topic sentence.

I (Identify the item)	V (select Verb)	F (Finish your thought)
"Batty About Bats!"	tells	
		the lengthy process of digging up dinosaur bones and putting them on display.
"Gemini: The Twins"		

Verb Bank

explains	tells	shows	provides	presents
describes	gives	compares	lists	teaches

Word Fluency

Read the words fluently.

	Correct	Errors
1st Try		
2nd Try		

stuck	bull	smog	quacking	got	gum	snip	slit	yams	cabs	10
smog	quacking	got	gum	snip	slit	yams	cabs	mix	bugs	20
got	gum	snip	slit	yams	cabs	mix	bugs	pulling	spots	30
snip	slit	yams	cabs	mix	bugs	pulling	spots	smack	span	40
yams	cabs	mix	bugs	pulling	spots	smack	span	rock	still	50
mix	bugs	pulling	spots	smack	span	rock	still	skins	fox	60
pulling	spots	smack	span	rock	still	skins	fox	bull	stuck	70
smack	span	rock	still	skins	fox	bull	stuck	quacking	smog	80
rock	still	skins	fox	bull	stuck	quacking	smog	gum	got	90
skins	fox	bull	stuck	quacking	smog	gum	got	slit	snip	100

Synonyms

Listen to the word. Choose the synonym from the word bank and write it on the line.

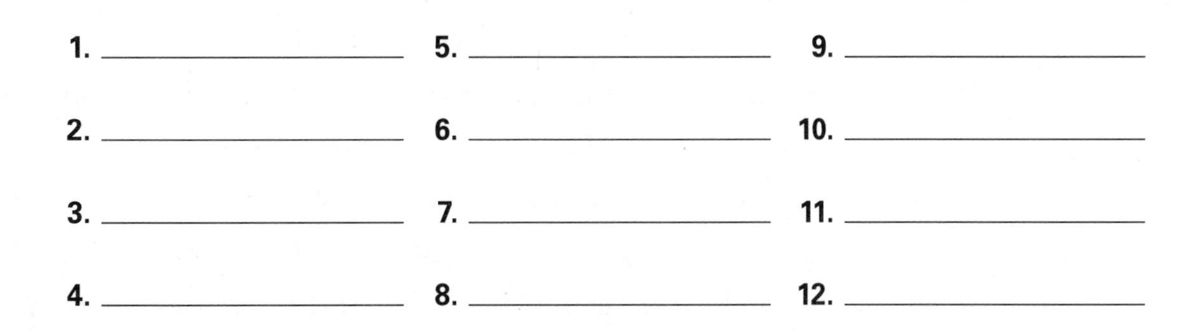

1. ____________ 5. ____________ 9. ____________

2. ____________ 6. ____________ 10. ____________

3. ____________ 7. ____________ 11. ____________

4. ____________ 8. ____________ 12. ____________

Word Bank

mad	slim	sack	snip	big	pull
cap	odd	pick	pal	small	sick

Sort It: *When, Where, or How*

Read the passage. Decide whether the underlined words and phrases tell *when, where,* or *how.* Write the words or phrases in the correct column.

Earthly Twins

Elvis Presley was born a twin in 1935 in Mississippi. Unfortunately, his twin Jesse died at birth. Elvis became famous. He went on to make music history. He got his start in music when he got a guitar for Christmas in 1946. From that beginning, Elvis went on to sell more records than anyone.

Kim and Kari Baker are also twins. These twins are ranchers and photographers. Born in Montana, they lived there until their teens, when they moved to Florida. There they developed a love for horses. In 1988, they returned to Montana and became ranchers. Their love of horses continues. Remarkably, horses can tell them apart, but people often can't!

When	Where	How

Question Words

Read the questions. Circle the question word. Write what the answer must include.

Question Words	How to Answer
If the question asks . . .	**Your answer must include . . .**
who	information about a person or group
what	an action or name of a thing
when	a specific time, date, or event
where	a general location or specific place

Question Words	How to Answer
If the question asks . . .	**Your answer must include . . .**
is/are	a yes or a no answer plus explanation
do/does	a yes or a no answer plus explanation

Question Words	How to Answer
If the question asks . . .	**Your answer must include . . .**
why	a reason or explanation
how	the way something is done

1. Is the sky divided?

____

2. When can we see Gemini?

____

3. Why do people group stars?

____

4. How are are constellations named?

____

5. Where can we see Gemini: The Twins?

____

Phrase Fluency

Read each phrase fluently.

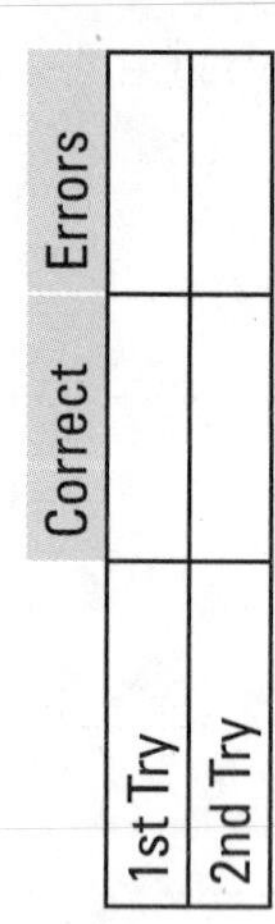

Phrase	Words	Phrase	Words
the sad man	3	up the big hill	80
the bad smog	6	Rick and Sam's	83
the hot yams	9	into the mix	86
pulling the dog	12	in the fog	89
by the rocks	15	the quacking ducks	92
the sick ox	18	in the dim cab	96
on the six mats	22	the full pack	99
Max is not	25	from the van	102
he was	27	for the cop	105
the fat fox	30	by the dock	108
Bob's big dog	33	in the pot	111
smacks his lips	36	Mom and Rod's van	115
at a stop	39	the full cup	118
into the pit	42	the dull bag	121
at the bus stop	46	the tan pup	124
on the box	49	a big bat	127
the fun gal	52	the sick kid's cup	131
from the pan	55	has six bills	134
the dull socks	58	the rats and cats	138
the bucking bull	61	by the fan	141
in the tin can	65	will snip the buds	145
the bad bugs	68	by his dad's box	149
on the spot	71	in the big sack	153
one box	73	in the mud	156
the quick dogs	76	at the dock	159

Answering Adverb Questions

Part A

Listen to each prepositional phrase and repeat it. Write the phrase on the line. Circle the preposition. If the phrase is acting as an adverb, write the question that it answers on the line to the right.

1. ______________________________ ____________

2. ______________________________ ____________

3. ______________________________ ____________

4. ______________________________ ____________

5. ______________________________ ____________

Part B

Choose two phrases from Part A and add to them to make them complete sentences. Write them below.

1. ______________________________________

2. ______________________________________

Sentence Morphs

Read the phrases. Scoop them in the complete sentences.

the rag doll was in the tan box The rag doll was in the tan box.	Did you spot the bugs in the pot Did you spot the bugs in the pot?	When I hit it the lock got stuck When I hit it, the lock got stuck.
The cop at the dock is standing by the cabs The cop at the dock is standing by the cabs.	Bob and Bill will jog up the hill in the smog Bob and Bill will jog up the hill in the smog.	The gulls nab the ham from the sack The gulls nab the ham from the sack.
Did the dog duck in the back of the van Did the dog duck in the back of the van?	The man is filling the hot dog buns The man is filling the hot dog buns.	Mom's tan van was pulling into the lot Mom's tan van was pulling into the lot.

Generating Questions

Read the sentences. Determine what question the sentence answers. Write the question and include necessary punctuation.

1. Sarah went to the store because she needed sugar and chocolate chips.

____

____

2. The test is on Friday.

____

____

3. They played tag in the park.

____

____

4. No, I am not going with you.

____

5. Dan is on the phone.

____

____

6. Mary jogged slowly.

____

____

7. Yes, Bill has a cat.

____

____

8. Sam watched his favorite show.

____

____

Define It

Determine the category and attributes of each word. Then, write the definition.

Word		Category		Attributes
shield	=		+	

Definition:

____

____

Word		Category		Attributes
battle	=		+	

Definition:

____

____

Word		Category		Attributes
square	=		+	

Definition:

____

____

Word		Category		Attributes
god	=		+	

Definition:

____

____

Close Reading: Guided Highlighting

Read the text and complete the tasks.

Gemini: The Twins

On a dark night, turn your eyes up to the sky. The **constellation** Gemini is a sight to see. It has two very bright stars called the Twins. People have known about them for thousands of years. They have been in the sky as long as anyone can remember.

What Are Constellations?

5 Constellations are fascinating and helpful to many people. They are **patterns** of stars that people see in the sky. These star patterns were invented by people fascinated with the stars. **Ancient poets** of different cultures made up stories about them. Sailors used the stars to navigate across the oceans. Farmers used the stars to tell them when to plant and 10 when to harvest because the same patterns appear in the sky during the same season every year. How long have we been seeing patterns in the night sky? We have done it for at least 6,000 years.

- **Write an IVF topic sentence for the second paragraph.** Refer to page 91 if needed. ______________________________

____

Why Did the Idea of Constellations Begin?

Constellations are groups of stars with a purpose. Why were star groups made up? There are so many stars! How could we remember them all? We 15 could put them in groups. The groups break the sky into parts. The stars in the sky are divided into 88 constellations. They help us remember which stars are which. How many stars can we see? On a dark night, we see 1,000 to 1,500 stars. Where can we see the Twins? We can see them in the northern hemisphere in November through April. We can see them in the 20 southern hemisphere in December through March.

- **Write an IVF topic sentence for this section.** Refer to page 91 if needed. ______________________________

____

____

Close Reading: Guided Highlighting (*cont.*)

The Ancient Stories of Gemini

Ancient people invented stories about the Gemini Twins. The Egyptians called them twin plants. The Hindus called them twin gods. Arabs called them twin peacocks. What is the ancient Greek story of Gemini? The Greeks said they were the sons of the Greek god Zeus and the woman
25 Leda. They said that Zeus and Leda had twin sons. Their names were Castor and Pollux. They were **devoted** and loving brothers. They looked alike. But they were not alike. Castor was **mortal** like his mother. He became a horseman. Pollux was immortal like his father. He became a boxer. Both became **expert** soldiers. Castor was killed in battle. Pollux
30 could not bear to be without his twin. Pollux asked his father, Zeus, for help. He asked for Castor to come back to life. Zeus let them be together side by side forever. They are the Twins that shine brightly in the sky. They are the two **brilliant** stars in Gemini.

Retell the story about the Greek twins, Castor and Pollux, by completing the charts. Some sections have been completed for you.

How were Castor and Pollux the same?

How were the twins different?	
Castor	**Pollux**
like his mother, Leda	like his father, ______
______	immortal
horseman	______

How did they become Gemini?	
Problem: ______ ______ ______ ______	Solution: ______ ______ ______ ______

Close Reading: Guided Highlighting (*cont.*)

Look Up

When you look up on a dark night, the sky is flooded with star patterns
35 that tell a story.

- Ursa Major (The Great Bear) is identified by the square of the Big Dipper, which forms the bear's body, and a chain of stars, which forms its tail. Ursa Major can be seen in the northern sky throughout the year.
- 40 Ursa Minor (Lesser Bear) is identified by the square of the Little Dipper, which forms the bear's body, and a chain of stars, which forms its tail. Ursa Minor can be seen in the northern sky. The North Star is part of this constellation. This bright star has been helpful to nighttime travelers for centuries.
- 45 Orion (The Hunter) has some of the brightest stars. He is positioned in the sky to fight off a raging bull. Orion stands with his right arm holding a great club uplifted in the air, ready to strike. Over his left arm hangs a lion's skin that he holds up as a shield in front of him to stop the raging bull. Taurus the Mighty 50 Bull is a constellation that is charging right for Orion. Orion is visible throughout the world. We can see this constellation between December and April.
- Leo (The Lion) is one of the easiest constellations to find. An easy way to spot Leo is to look for a backward question mark in the sky, 55 which represents the head and front of the body. In the northern hemisphere, Leo can be located in spring, and in the southern hemisphere it can be located in autumn.
- Centaurus (The Centaur) has the greatest number of visible stars in it. It has 101 stars.
- 60 Hydra (The Water Snake) is the largest constellation. It covers more than 3% of the sky.

- **Write an IVF topic sentence for this section.** Refer to page 91 if needed. ______________________________

____

Ask and Answer Questions

Reread "Gemini: The Twins." After each section, write a question for your partner to answer using question words that you have learned so far. Try not to use the same question word twice. Be prepared to answer your question orally. Use the chart on page 14 to help you.

Introduction *Who?* *What?*

1. ______________________________

____

What Are Constellations? *What?* *When?*

2. ______________________________

____

Why Did the Idea of Constellations Begin? *How?* *When?*

3. ______________________________

____

The Ancient Stories of Gemini *Who?* *What?*

4. ______________________________

____

Look Up (Write two questions for this section.) *Where?* *How?* *Who?* *When?*

5. ______________________________

____

____

____

Passage Comprehension

Underline the question word in each question. Then, answer each question using a complete sentence. Write the evidence from the text.

1. What is Gemini?

____

____

Text Evidence: ______________________________

____

____

2. How were constellations helpful?

____

____

____

Text Evidence: ______________________________

____

____

3. Why did the idea of constellations begin?

____

____

____

Text Evidence: ______________________________

____

____

4. Where can Gemini be seen?

____

____

____

Text Evidence: ______________________________

____

____

Passage Comprehension (*cont.*)

5. What did different cultures say about the Gemini Twins?

Text Evidence:

6. How were Castor and Pollux alike?

Text Evidence:

7. What constellation is attacking another constellation in the sky?

Text Evidence:

8. Is the North Star a constellation? Are the Twins a constellation?

Text Evidence:

Four-Square

Write the definition of *mortal*. Then, write examples, synonyms, and antonyms of the word in the appropriate boxes.

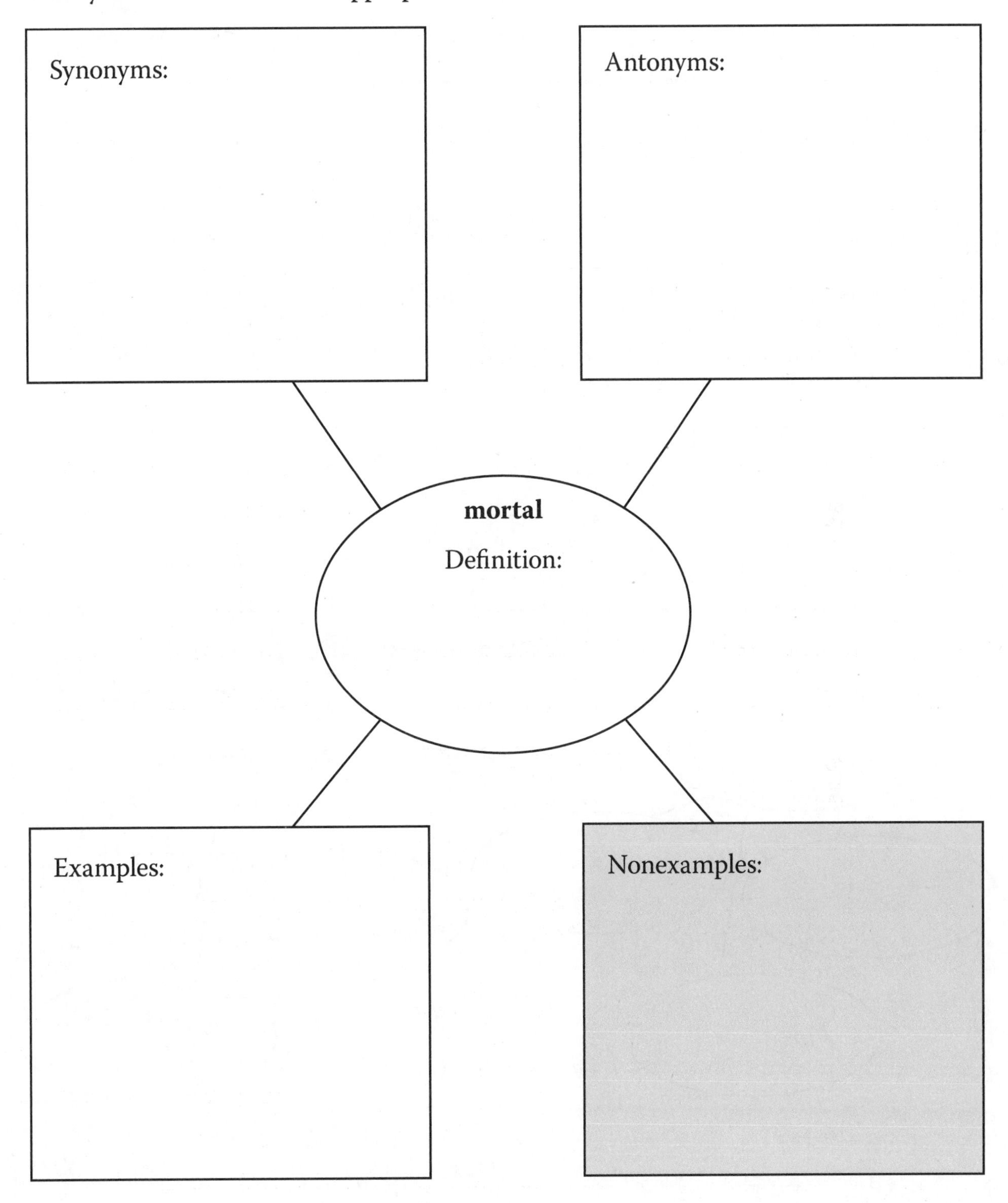

Making Connections

Make connections to the word *myth* by mapping other words related to the word.

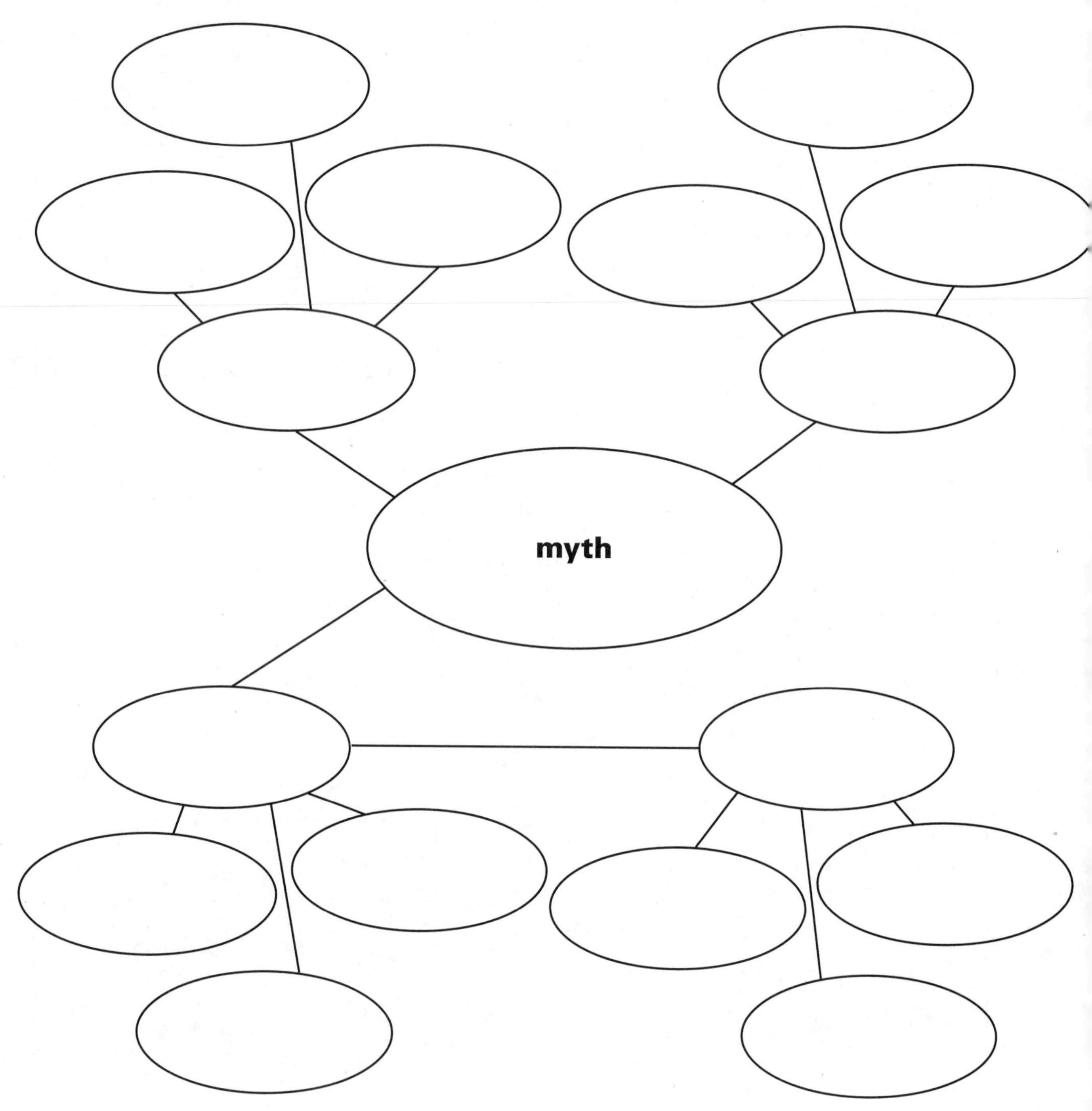

Direct Objects

Part A

Fill in the chart for each sentence using the questions from Masterpiece Sentences. Write *subject, predicate,* or *direct object* to indicate the sentence element that was added to complete each sentence.

Who or What did it?	What did they do?	What did they do it to?	Sentence Element
ancient people	invented		
	used	the stars for planting	
people		the stars	
constellations	divide		
ancient poets	write		

Part B

Add a direct object to each sentence. The question after each sentence provides a clue.

1. The boys played ________________________. (What did they play?)
2. After dinner, we watched ________________________. (What did we watch?)
3. Each morning, Bill and Beth run ________________________. (What do they run?)
4. My mother painted ________________________. (What did she paint?)
5. The students asked ________________________. (What did they ask?)

Word Functions

Part A

Read the sentences. Circle "Noun" or "Verb" for the underlined word.

1. He dips his hand into the damp sand. Noun or Verb
2. We had dips with our chips. Noun or Verb
3. Dan's cat did tricks. Noun or Verb
4. Dan tricks his twin. Noun or Verb
5. The tracks are in the sand. Noun or Verb
6. The cat tracks sand in the house. Noun or Verb

Part B

Write two sentences for each word. In the first sentence, use the word as a noun. In the second sentence, use the word as a verb.

1. cracks: ______________________________

   cracks: ______________________________
2. kicks: ______________________________

   kicks: ______________________________
3. snacks: ______________________________

   snacks: ______________________________
4. backs: ______________________________

   backs: ______________________________
5. packs: ______________________________

   packs: ______________________________

Word Fluency

Read the words fluently.

	Correct	Errors
1st Try		
2nd Try		

stuck	bull	smog	quacking	got	gum	snip	slit	yams	cabs	10
smog	quacking	got	gum	snip	slit	yams	cabs	mix	bugs	20
got	gum	snip	slit	yams	cabs	mix	bugs	pulling	spots	30
snip	slit	yams	cabs	mix	bugs	pulling	spots	smack	span	40
yams	cabs	mix	bugs	pulling	spots	smack	span	rock	still	50
mix	bugs	pulling	spots	smack	span	rock	still	skins	fox	60
pulling	spots	smack	span	rock	still	skins	fox	bull	stuck	70
smack	span	rock	still	skins	fox	bull	stuck	quacking	smog	80
rock	still	skins	fox	bull	stuck	quacking	smog	gum	got	90
skins	fox	bull	stuck	quacking	smog	gum	got	slit	snip	100

Blueprint for Reading: Main Idea

Highlight the **main ideas** in green. Highlight the **key details** in yellow.

based on "Gemini: The Twins"

On a dark night, turn your eyes up to the dark sky. The constellation Gemini is a sight to see. It has two very bright stars called the Twins. People have known about them for thousands of years. They have been in the sky as long as anyone can remember.

What Are Constellations?

Constellations are fascinating and helpful to many people. They are patterns of stars that people see in the sky. These star patterns were invented by people fascinated with the stars. Ancient poets of different cultures made up stories about them. Sailors use the stars to navigate. Farmers use the stars to tell them when to plant and when to harvest because the same patterns appear in the sky in the same seasons every year. How long have we been seeing patterns in the night sky? We have done it for at least 6,000 years.

Why Did the Idea of Constellations Begin?

Constellations are groups of stars with a purpose. There are so many stars! How could we remember them all? We could put them in groups. The groups break the sky into parts. The stars in the sky are divided into 88 constellations. They help us remember which stars are which. How many stars can we see? On a dark night, we see 1,000 to 1,500 stars. Where can we see the Twins? We can see them in the northern hemisphere in November through April. We can see them in the southern hemisphere in December through March.

Blueprint for Reading: Main Idea (*cont.*)

The Ancient Stories of Gemini

Ancient people invented stories about the Gemini Twins. The Egyptians called them twin plants. The Hindus called them twin gods. Arabs called them twin peacocks. What is the ancient Greek story of Gemini? The Greeks said they were the sons of the Greek god Zeus and the woman Leda. They said that Zeus and Leda had twin sons. Their names were Castor and Pollux. They were devoted and loving brothers. They looked alike. But they were not alike. Castor was mortal like his mother. He became a horseman. Pollux was immortal like his father. He became a boxer. Both became expert soldiers. Castor was killed in battle. Pollux could not bear to be without his twin. Pollux asked his father, Zeus, for help. He asked for Castor to come back to life. Zeus let them be together side by side forever. They are the Twins that shine brightly in the sky. They are the two brilliant stars in Gemini.

Blueprint for Reading: Main Idea (*cont.*)

Look Up

When you look up on a dark night, the sky is flooded with star patterns that tell a story. Ursa Major (The Great Bear) is identified by the square of the Big Dipper, which forms the bear's body, and a chain of stars, which forms its tail. Ursa Major can be seen in the northern sky throughout the year. Ursa Minor (Lesser Bear) is identified by the square of the Little Dipper, which forms the bear's body, and a chain of stars, which forms its tail. Ursa Minor can be seen in the northern sky. The North Star is part of this constellation. This bright star has been helpful to nighttime travelers for centuries. Orion (The Hunter) has some of the brightest stars. He is positioned in the sky to fight off a raging bull. Orion stands with his right arm holding a great club uplifted in the air, ready to strike. Over his left arm hangs a lion's skin that he holds up as a shield in front of him to stop the raging bull. Taurus the Mighty Bull is a constellation that is charging right for Orion. Orion is visible throughout the world. We can see this constellation between December and April. Leo (The Lion) is one of the easiest constellations to find. An easy way to spot Leo is to look for a backward question mark in the sky, which represents the head and front of the body. In the northern hemisphere, Leo can be located in spring, and in the southern hemisphere it can be located in autumn. Centaurus (The Centaur) has the greatest number of visible stars in it. It has 101 stars. Hydra (The Water Snake) is the largest constellation. It covers more than 3% of the sky.

Blueprint for Writing: Main Idea

Write the main ideas and key details to help you retell the passage and write a summary.

Turn a Prompt into a Topic Sentence

Read each prompt. Circle the words that define the topic. Underline the direction words and then write a topic sentence that addresses the prompt.

1. Prompt: Write a paragraph that explains how scientists dig for dinosaur bones.

   Digging for dinosaur bones involves ______________________________

   ____

2. Prompt: Pretend that you could be mayor of your town or city for a day. In a paragraph, explain what you would do as mayor for a day.

   As mayor for a day, ____

   ____

3. Prompt: Write a paragraph that describes a fair way to divide a group of students into two sports team.

   ____

   ____

4. Prompt: Think of your best friend. In a paragraph, describe what makes your best friend special.

   ____

   ____

5. Prompt: Write a movie review that explains to others what your favorite movie is and why.

   ____

   ____

Using New Vocabulary

Fill in the blanks with the appropriate vocabulary words. If you need assistance, use the word bank at the bottom of the page.

Some of the ancient stories were told by ______________. They told stories about the beautiful ______________ of stars in the sky. The Greeks told a story about ______________ soldiers who were brothers. They were excellent soldiers. Because Castor was ______________, he was killed in battle. However, his twin brother, Pollux, couldn't die. He missed his brother deeply. Pollux was broken-hearted and so ______________ to his twin that he asked his father, Zeus, to bring Castor back to life. The ______________ story passed down for hundreds of years says that instead they became part of the ______________ Gemini. When you look up, the twin brothers are the two ______________ stars resting side by side in the night sky.

Word Bank

devoted	patterns	mortal	poets
constellation	brilliant	ancient	expert

Reading for Fluency

Read the passage with prosody. Chunk the words into phrases and create an image in your head as you read.

The Big Dogs and the Rams

One pack of kids has the tan Big Dogs hats. Rick, Tim, Kim, Mick, and Ron are the Big Dogs. One pack of kids is the Rams. Bill, Dan, Sal, Jan, and Nan are the Rams.

The Big Dogs are at bat and Tim is up. He hits it to the man at the bag. The man stops it. Tim runs back to the pit. Rick is at bat for the Big Dogs. He is the top hit man for the Big Dogs. Hit it big, Rick. Hit it to the back of the bags. The fans are pulling for you. Rick hits. Up it pops. Where is it? It hits in a spot in back of the bags. Rick jogs the bags for one run. Kim hits it to the man at the bag. He snags it. Kim runs back in the pit. Ron digs in. He hits. It hops on the sod to the man at the bag. Just one run is bad for the Big Dogs.

The Rams are at bat. Dan pops it to the back. He runs to the bag. Sal hits it and jogs to the bag. Bill pops it up, and runs into the man on the bag. He is mad as he runs back to the pit. Jan pops it up. The man gets it. Jan runs back to the pit. The Rams are in a bad spot. Just one run and the Rams will win. Can the Rams do it? Nan is up to bat. Pick a fat one, Nan. You can do it. Rip the hit to the back. Bam! Tim is in the back. It hits him on the lip. He ducks. He cannot stop it. Nan jogs the bags for one run. What a hit. The Rams win! It is a mob in the pit. Live it up, kids.

Answering Questions

Listen to the prompts and possible answers. Fill in the bubble for your answer choice.

Example: Do all groups of stars have stories about them?

To answer this question, I need to include _____.

- Ⓐ a yes or no answer, plus an explanation
- Ⓑ information about a person or group
- Ⓒ an action or name of a thing
- Ⓓ a specific time, date, or event

1. Who said that the Twins were peacocks?

To answer this question, I need to include _____.

- Ⓐ a general location or specific place
- Ⓑ an action or name of a thing
- Ⓒ information about a person or group
- Ⓓ a yes or no answer, plus an explanation

2. What group of stars is named after a lion?

To answer this question, I need to include _____.

- Ⓐ information about a person or group
- Ⓑ an action or name of a thing
- Ⓒ the way something is done
- Ⓓ a yes or no answer, plus an explanation

3. Does Orion have only three stars?

To answer this question, I need to include _____.

- Ⓐ information about a person or group
- Ⓑ an action or name of a thing
- Ⓒ a yes or no answer, plus an explanation
- Ⓓ a specific time, date, or event

4. When can the Big Dipper be seen in the northern sky?

To answer this question, I need to include _____.

- Ⓐ a specific time, date, or event
- Ⓑ an action or name of a thing
- Ⓒ information about a person or group
- Ⓓ a yes or no answer, plus an explanation

5. Where is a constellation Orion?

To answer this question, I need to include _____.

- Ⓐ information about a person or group
- Ⓑ a reason or explanation
- Ⓒ a yes or no answer, plus an explanation
- Ⓓ a general location or specific place

Prepositions

Listen to the prompts and possible answers. Fill in the bubble for your answer choice.

Example: Choose the best preposition to complete the following sentence:

The dog jumped _____ the water.

Ⓐ behind
Ⓑ below
Ⓒ by
Ⓓ into

1. Choose the best preposition to complete the following sentence:

   His fork fell _____ the floor.

   Ⓐ onto
   Ⓑ under
   Ⓒ into
   Ⓓ above

2. Choose the best preposition to complete the following sentence:

   The ice cream is _____ the freezer.

   Ⓐ over
   Ⓑ past
   Ⓒ until
   Ⓓ in

3. Choose the best preposition to complete the following sentence:

   Walt was happy standing _____ his two best friends.

   Ⓐ underneath
   Ⓑ between
   Ⓒ from
   Ⓓ on

4. Choose the best preposition to comple the following sentence:

   Who left the door _____ the garage open?

   Ⓐ for
   Ⓑ without
   Ⓒ with
   Ⓓ to

5. Choose the best preposition to comple the following sentence:

   My favorite book is _____ two rabbits.

   Ⓐ about
   Ⓑ off
   Ⓒ over
   Ⓓ into

Words with Multiple Functions

Listen to the questions and possible answers. Fill in the bubble for your answer choice.

Example: In which sentence is the word *fall* a noun?

- Ⓐ The weather starts getting cold in the fall.
- Ⓑ Clowns fall down as part of his act.
- Ⓒ My friends fall into step with me and we keep walking.
- Ⓓ The fort will fall unless help arrives.

1. In which sentence is the word *stick* a noun?

- Ⓐ James hung the picture with tape, but it didn't stick.
- Ⓑ The dart will stick if you throw it hard enough.
- Ⓒ Freda used a stick to stir up the fire.
- Ⓓ Even though running a mile was hard, Karla decided to stick with it.

2. In which sentence is the word *start* a noun?

- Ⓐ The race will start in five minutes.
- Ⓑ Boys start to have beards when they become teens.
- Ⓒ The loud bang made me start.
- Ⓓ It was the start of a new day.

3. In which sentence is the word *order* a verb?

- Ⓐ My room was in perfect order when I left for school.
- Ⓑ I will order a hot dog.
- Ⓒ We called our club "The Order of the Slingshot."
- Ⓓ Please keep the cards in order by number.

4. In which sentence is the word *scale* a verb?

- Ⓐ As a final test, we had to scale a wall.
- Ⓑ We looked at a fish scale in science class.
- Ⓒ The jazz player invented a new musical scale.
- Ⓓ On a scale of one to ten, how much does your finger hurt?

5. In which sentence is the word *form* a verb?

- Ⓐ We had to fill out a form at the doctor's office.
- Ⓑ First, we form the clay into a ball.
- Ⓒ The runner was in top form for the race.
- Ⓓ What form of dance do you do?

Synonyms

Listen to the questions and possible answers. Fill in the bubble for your answer choice.

Example: Which word is a synonym for *street*?

- Ⓐ sidewalk
- Ⓑ road
- Ⓒ railroad
- Ⓓ alley

1. Which word is a synonym for *woods*?

- Ⓐ tree
- Ⓑ hillside
- Ⓒ forest
- Ⓓ trail

2. Which word is a synonym for *final*?

- Ⓐ last
- Ⓑ middle
- Ⓒ beginning
- Ⓓ continuous

3. Which word is a synonym for *leap*?

- Ⓐ step
- Ⓑ jump
- Ⓒ trip
- Ⓓ fall

4. Which word is a synonym for *giggle*?

- Ⓐ laugh
- Ⓑ talk
- Ⓒ cry
- Ⓓ gab

5. Which word is a synonym for *speak*?

- Ⓐ yell
- Ⓑ whisper
- Ⓒ stutter
- Ⓓ talk

Let's Focus: "Jazz: The Recipe"

Content Focus
jazz music

Type of Text
informational

Author's Purpose
to inform

Big Ideas
Consider the following Big Idea questions. Write your answer for each question.

Where did jazz music come from?

____

____

Why do people make music?

____

____

Informational Preview Checklist: "Jazz: The Recipe" on pages 125 and 126.

- ☐ Title: What clue does it provide about the passage?
- ☐ Pictures and Captions: What additional information is added here?
- ☐ Headings: What topics will this text include?
- ☐ Margin Information: What vocabulary is important to understand this text?
- ☐ Maps, Charts, Graphs: Are additional visuals present that will help me understand?

Reading for a Purpose

1. Where did workers sing work songs?
2. What did African Americans do to change church music?
3. What stories do ballads tell?
4. Why were freed slaves singing the blues?
5. Where did all the different music come together?
6. What were the ingredients that made up the jazz recipe?
7. Why is New Orleans considered the "Melting Pot of Sound"?

Key Passage Vocabulary: "Jazz: The Recipe"

Rate your knowledge of the words. Define the words. Draw a picture to help you remember the definition.

Vocabulary	Knowledge Rating	Definition	Picture
recipe	0 1 2 3		
steady	0 1 2 3		
simple	0 1 2 3		
plantation	0 1 2 3		
social	0 1 2 3		
demand	0 1 2 3		
combine	0 1 2 3		
express	0 1 2 3		

Jazz: The Recipe

Jazz began with a "**recipe**" that had many different ingredients. Different groups of people, including Africans and Europeans, were part of the recipe. Different kinds of music, including the blues and ragtime, were also a part of the recipe. All of these ingredients combined to make America's own music, jazz.

recipe
a list of the things needed and directions for making something

Workers sang songs during the long workday. They sang in fields and on ships. They sang while working on the railroads. The work song was an important part of their day. With tools in their hands, they worked to a **steady** beat. The songs made life a little easier. There were many kinds of work songs, and these songs played a part in jazz.

steady
not subject to change; constant

Church music was important to jazz. African Americans made new kinds of church music. They formed their own churches and rewrote the old songs to express their faith. They changed the words, the beat, and the tune. They used the African "call and response" when they sang. This music became an ingredient in the jazz recipe.

simple
having few parts; easy to understand

plantation
a large farm where crops are grown

social
friendly; involving several people

demand
requirement; need

combine
to put together; to join

express
to communicate in words

Music of immigrant Americans added to jazz. The Scotch-Irish had ballads. Ballads tell stories of heroes and their bravery, and these stories are often sad. The song is usually **simple**. In a ballad, the story is often more important than the music. Ballads became another ingredient in the jazz recipe.

In the early days of America, ballroom dance music provided popular entertainment. In the South, dances were held on **plantations**. They were big **social** events. There was a **demand** for musicians to play at the dances. Many slaves learned how to play fiddles and flutes. African Americans invented the banjo and played it too. Black musicians learned the dance songs and changed them. African and European music **combined** to make dance music. This music became another ingredient in the jazz recipe.

During the 1800s, a new kind of music called ragtime was born. It was loud and fun. Musicians pounded on their pianos. They made up songs to **express** their appreciation for music. They played in dance halls. The tunes were lively, and the rhythm was catchy. Everybody loved ragtime. It had a strong, irregular beat that was surprising. Ragtime became another ingredient in the jazz recipe.

Sometime in the late 1800s, musicians began to play the blues. Slaves had been freed, but life was still hard. People were sad and frustrated. They expressed their feelings in music. They called it the blues. Today, people still sing the blues when they're sad. The blues became the final ingredient in the recipe.

The jazz recipe came together in New Orleans. By 1890, New Orleans was one of America's most musical cities. It had opera houses and concert halls. It had dance ballrooms and street parades. It had Mardi Gras! Many different people lived there. Africans and Native Americans lived in New Orleans. The French and Spanish also lived there. People from many places and cultures created America's own music, jazz.

Adapted with permission from "Jazz Ingredients"
by Heather Mitchell Amey

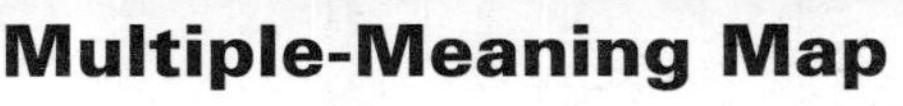

Multiple-Meaning Map

Determine the meanings of the word *jazz*. Write the definitions in the boxes. Use the word in a sentence on the lines below the boxes.

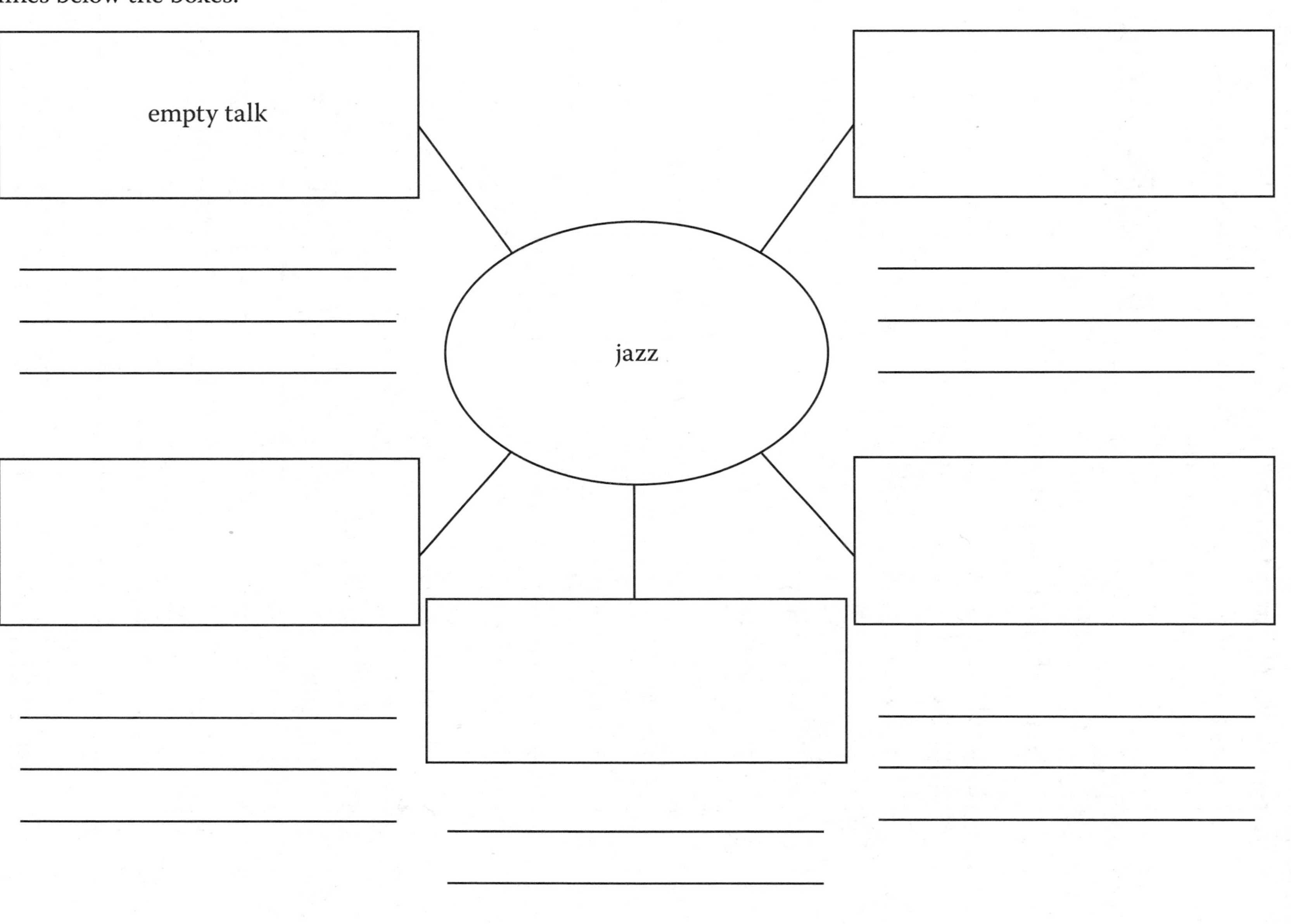

Identify It: Noun or Verb

Read each pair of sentences. Decide if the bold word is a noun or a verb. Then, place an X in the proper column.

	Noun	Verb
1. She **licks** the candy.		
It takes 20 **licks** to finish the candy.		
2. The car made two **stops** on the trip.		
The car **stops** at the corner.		
3. The **rack** of hats is full.		
They **rack** the hats at night.		
4. She **blocks** him.		
She has six **blocks**.		
5. The ships stop at the **docks**.		
The ship **docks** here.		
6. Dad **grills** hot dogs.		
The **grills** were hot.		
7. He **spots** the asp in the grass.		
There are **spots** on that asp.		
8. We have trick **locks**.		
She **locks** the gift in the attic.		

Sort It: *When, Where,* or *How*

Read the passage. Decide if the underlined words and phrases tell *when, where,* or *how.* Write the words or phrases in the correct column.

What a Wonderful World of Jazz

Jazz is a popular style of music in Louisiana. Thankfully, there are many local musicians who play. They play at clubs. They play in the streets. They play on the radio.

Jazz became a part of Louisiana culture in 1890. From the beginning, jazz has entertained residents, visitors, and people from all cultures.

Louis Armstrong is possibly the most popular jazz musician in the world. Born in Louisiana, Armstrong grew up poor and troubled. He learned to play the cornet at school in his early teens. However, Armstrong was too poor to buy an instrument of his own. Luckily, after leaving school at the age of 14, he spent time with a jazz musician who taught him and gave him his first instrument. With hard work, Armstrong became a respected musician and began playing with bands in local clubs.

Armstrong lived in Louisiana until jazz music took him to St. Louis, Chicago, and all over the world. He recorded 12 albums and his song "What a Wonderful World" can be heard on countless movies, television shows, and commercials. Eventually, Armstrong died at the age of 70 in New York. Louis Armstrong's music and influence on jazz cannot be matched.

When	Where	How

The E's: Examples, Explanations, and Evidence

The paragraph below has a topic sentence and supporting details. Use the elaborations provided to complete the paragraph.

Possible E's

For example, it causes lung cancer.

Smoke that affects other people is called secondhand smoke.

Smoking also caused three of the worst wildfires in California between 1929 and 1999.

Secondhand smoke can harm the health of those around the person who is smoking.

It is also a major cause of heart disease.

Smoking is the leading cause of fire deaths.

Smoking causes a number of problems. First, smoking pollutes the air that others breathe. ______________________________

____

____

____

Second, smoking can be a fire hazard. ______________________________

____

____

____

Third, smoking can cause illnesses. ______________________________

____

____

____

______________________________ Smoking is a dangerous habit.

Word Fluency

Read the words fluently.

	Correct	Errors
1st Try		
2nd Try		

socks	fuzz	stuff	fast	yell	puffs	missing	spilled	pass	desk	10
stuff	fast	yell	puffs	missing	spilled	pass	desk	fixed	pulled	20
yell	puffs	missing	spilled	pass	desk	fixed	pulled	telling	off	30
missing	spilled	pass	desk	fixed	pulled	telling	off	gasp	snack	40
pass	desk	fixed	pulled	telling	off	gasp	snack	slots	quick	50
fixed	pulled	telling	off	gasp	snack	slots	quick	deck	boxing	60
telling	off	gasp	snack	slots	quick	deck	boxing	fuzz	socks	70
gasp	snack	slots	quick	deck	boxing	fuzz	socks	fast	stuff	80
slots	quick	deck	boxing	fuzz	socks	fast	stuff	puffs	yell	90
deck	boxing	fuzz	socks	fast	stuff	puffs	yell	spilled	missing	100

Nonexamples

Read the category. Then, read the list of words under the category. All of the words are examples, except for one. This word is a nonexample. Circle the nonexample in each set of words.

mammals	**constellation**
bat lizard tiger dog	Big Dipper Orion Ursa Major Ursa Minor
fragile porcelain doll glass house coffee mug plastic cup	**pattern** quilt constellation songs circle
ancient dinosaur bones mp3 players fossils mummies	**star** LeBron James your teacher Megan Fox Tom Cruise
brilliant cave star lamp flashlight	**expert** doctor lawyer baby professional athlete
sturdy brick house steel house wood house straw house	**mortal** teacher mom Zeus dad

Find It: Commas and Adverbial Phrases

Read each sentence. If the sentence begins with an adverbial phrase, underline the phrase and circle the comma. Every sentence has a comma in it, but not every sentence begins with an adverbial phrase. Write the prepositions from the underlined phrases on the line at the bottom of the page.

1. From the beginning of jazz, artists and photographers have tried to capture its spirit in art.
2. In the 1920s, there was a new spirit.
3. They did the Charleston, the most popular jazz dance.
4. By the 1940s, photography had improved.
5. Film was faster, and the flash became portable.
6. Over the years, artists and photographers have tried many ways to capture the look and feel of jazz.
7. The paintings and photographs are strong, alive, and free.
8. On August 4, 1901, Louis was born in New Orleans.
9. Within a year, he proudly led the band through his old neighborhood.
10. For the first time, he had regular meals and clean clothes.

Prepositions: ____

Choose It: Questions and Answers

Read each question. Circle the correct answer. Pay close attention to what the question is asking.

1. What time does class begin?
   a. Class begins with a warm-up exercise.
   b. The class is very difficult.
   c. Class begins at 9:00 a.m.
   d. That is my last class of the day.

2. Where did they find the dinosaur bones?
   a. It took a long time for them to find the bones.
   b. They had to dig very carefully to preserve the bones.
   c. The Touareg tribe helped them find the bones.
   d. They found the bones in the desert.

3. Are you going on the field trip?
   a. No, I have not been on a field trip.
   b. Yes, I like going on field trips.
   c. Yes, I am going on the field trip.
   d. No, I do not want to go on the field trip.

4. What is tonight's homework assignment?
   a. The assignment is written on the board.
   b. Tonight's assignment is to read pages 99–121.
   c. Tonight's assignment is going to be very time-consuming.
   d. I have so much homework tonight!

5. Who won the contest?
   a. Seventeen people entered the contest.
   b. Sarah did not enter the contest.
   c. Beth and Stan wanted Melissa to win the contest.
   d. Jill won the contest and Hank came in second place.

6. How do I look?
   a. It looks scary.
   b. You look pretty.
   c. They look sad.
   d. We look carefully at the paper.

Phrase Fluency

Read each phrase fluently.

	Correct	Errors
1st Try		
2nd Try		

Phrase	Words	Phrase	Words
at dusk	2	a buzz cut	83
as well as she can	7	a tan bell	86
to the back pen	11	by the buff men	90
Dad's full cup	14	for your mom	93
from the west	17	his wet socks	96
in my desk	20	into my spot	99
into the well	23	Jeff's pet cat	102
kicked well	25	less mess	104
off the deck	28	on his cell	107
one speck	30	onto his back	110
on top of the hill	35	not on his leg	114
not telling yet	38	past the nets	117
ran fast	40	Russ's big dog	120
Sam's best vest	43	she is not	123
sick of the smell	47	on six tests	126
still spilled	49	Tess's best stuff	129
ten tasks	51	the dim well	132
the duck's back	54	the fat hogs	135
the hot rocks	57	on the red steps	139
the sad doll with	61	the sick gal said	143
the fat duck's leg	65	to get a pen	147
to our sled	68	up your leg	150
up to the wet jet	73	was packing last	153
was spilling less	76	the wet pet's smell	157
with your fun pal	80	on the fat hog's back	162

Phrase Dictation: Adverbs

Part A

Listen to each phrase and repeat it. Write it on the line. Place an X to show which question the phrase answers.

Phrase	When	Where	How
1.			
2.			
3.			
4.			
5.			

Part B

Use the phrases to complete the following sentences:

1. Jill sat ____.
2. Sam ____.
3. We ran ____.
4. The bug hopped __________________________________.
5. Bill's cup ____________________________ than Tom's cup.

Sentence Morphs

Read the phrases. Scoop them in the complete sentences.

• Jim's stuff • • was spilling • • onto the steps • Jim's stuff was spilling onto the steps.	• The fat hogs • • will nap • • in the slop • The fat hogs will nap in the slop.	• He kicked • • his wet socks • • onto the bed • He kicked his wet socks onto the bed.
• As she fell • • off the deck • • Bess yelled • As she fell off the deck, Bess yelled.	• The red van • • did laps • • in the wet mud • The red van did laps in the wet mud.	• Ned and Ted • • sped by • • in the sled • Ned and Ted sped by in the sled.
• When he fell • • Jeff checked his leg • • for cuts • When he fell, Jeff checked his leg for cuts.	• The ten chicks • • were kicking up • • specks of dust • The ten chicks were kicking up specks of dust.	• The six kids • • were packing • • and missed the bus • The six kids were packing and missed the bus.

Questions and Answers

Use the picture to ask questions using *who, what, when, where, how,* and *why.* Answer the questions.

1. Who is involved in the recycling project? Students from Mrs. Jones's class are involved in the project.

2. What are they recycling? The students are recycling the newspapers they use in class.

3. When did they begin the project? They began the project when school started.

4. How are they collecting the newspapers? Each class has a special recycling bin and a representative to monitor the recycling.

5. Where do they take the paper? They take the paper to the local recycling center.

6. Why are they doing this project? The students wanted to help reduce waste and they are earning money at the same time.

1. ____________________

2. ____________________

3. ____________________

4. ____________________

5. ____________________

6. ____________________

Define It

Determine the category and attributes of each word. Then, write the definition.

Word		Category		Attributes
ballad	=		+	

Definition:

____

____

Word		Category		Attributes
musician	=		+	

Definition:

____

____

Word		Category		Attributes
banjo	=		+	

Definition:

____

____

Word		Category		Attributes
dance	=		+	

Definition:

____

____

Close Reading: Guided Highlighting

Read the text and complete the tasks.

Jazz: The Recipe

Headings	
African and European Music Unites	Immigrant Americans Add to the Recipe
African Americans Add to the Recipe	Ragtime Surprise!
The Melting Pot of Sound	Birth of Jazz
Singing the Blues	The Song of the Worker

____

Jazz began with a **"recipe"** that had many different ingredients. Different groups of people, including Africans and Europeans, were part of the recipe. Different kinds of music, including the blues and ragtime, were also a part of the recipe. All of these ingredients combined to make America's own music, jazz.

____

5 Workers sang songs during the long workday. They sang in fields and on ships. They sang while working on the railroads. The work song was an important part of their day. With tools in their hands, they worked to a **steady** beat. The songs made life a little easier. There were many kinds of work songs, and these songs played a part in jazz.

____

10 Church music was important to jazz. African Americans made new kinds of church music. They formed their own churches and rewrote the old songs to express their faith. They changed the words, the beat, and the tune. They used the African "call and response" when they sang. This music became an ingredient in the jazz recipe.

____

15 Music of immigrant Americans added to jazz. The Scotch-Irish had ballads. Ballads tell stories of heroes and their bravery, and these stories are often sad. The song is usually **simple**. In a ballad, the story is often more important than the music. Ballads became another ingredient in the jazz recipe.

Close Reading: Guided Highlighting (*cont.*)

In the early days of America, ballroom dance music provided popular
20 entertainment. In the South, dances were held on **plantations**. They were big **social** events. There was a **demand** for musicians to play at the dances. Many slaves learned how to play fiddles and flutes. African Americans invented the banjo and played it too. Black musicians learned the dance songs and changed them. African and European music **combined** to make
25 dance music. This music became another ingredient in the jazz recipe.

During the 1800s, a new kind of music called ragtime was born. It was loud and fun. Musicians pounded on their pianos. They made up songs to **express** their appreciation for music. They played in dance halls. The tunes were lively, and the rhythm was catchy. Everybody loved ragtime.
30 It had a strong, irregular beat that was surprising. Ragtime became another ingredient in the jazz recipe.

Sometime in the late 1800s, musicians began to play the blues. Slaves had been freed, but life was still hard. People were sad and frustrated. They expressed their feelings in music. They called it the blues. Today, people
35 still sing the blues when they're sad. The blues became the final ingredient in the recipe.

The jazz recipe came together in New Orleans. By 1890, New Orleans was one of America's most musical cities. It had opera houses and concert halls. It had dance ballrooms and street parades. It had Mardi Gras!
40 Many different people lived there. Africans and Native Americans lived in New Orleans. The French and Spanish also lived there. People from many places and cultures created America's own music, jazz.

Masterpiece Sentences: Stage 3

Use the picture to answer the questions. Then, write a sentence that uses all the answers.

<table>
<tr><th>Who or What did it?</th><th>What did they (he/she/it) do?</th><th>What did they (he/she/it) do it to?</th></tr>
<tr><td rowspan="7"></td><td></td><td rowspan="7"></td></tr>
<tr><td>When?</td></tr>
<tr><td></td></tr>
<tr><td>Where?</td></tr>
<tr><td></td></tr>
<tr><td>How?</td></tr>
<tr><td></td></tr>
</table>

Final Sentence

____

____

Ask and Answer Questions

Reread "Jazz: The Recipe." After each section, write a question for your partner to answer using question words that you have learned so far. Use the chart on page 14 to help you. Try not to use the same question word twice. Be prepared to answer your question orally.

Paragraph 1 *Who?* *How?*

1. ______________________________

Paragraph 2 *Where?* *When?*

2. ______________________________

Paragraph 3 *What?* *Who?*

3. ______________________________

Paragraph 4 *Is?* *Do?*

4. ______________________________

Paragraph 5 *How?* *Where?*

5. ______________________________

Paragraph 6 *How?* *What?*

6. ______________________________

Paragraph 7 *Why?* *Who?*

7. ______________________________

Paragraph 8 *Who?* *Where?*

8. ______________________________

Passage Comprehension

Underline the question word in each question. Then, answer each question using a complete sentence. Write the evidence from the text.

1. Where did workers sing work songs?

____

Text Evidence: ________________________________

____

2. What did African Americans do to change church music?

____

____

Text Evidence: ________________________________

____

____

3. What stories do ballads tell?

____

Text Evidence: ________________________________

____

4. Why were freed slaves singing the blues?

____

____

Text Evidence: ________________________________

____

5. Where did all the different music come together?

____

____

Text Evidence: ________________________________

____

Passage Comprehension (*cont.*)

6. What were the ingredients that made up the jazz recipe?

Text Evidence:

7. *Melting pot* is a metaphor, or figure of speech, that describes how different people come together to form a common culture. Why is New Orleans considered the "Melting Pot of Sound"?

Text Evidence:

Four-Square

Write the definition of *simple*. Then, write examples, nonexamples, synonyms, and antonyms of the word in the appropriate boxes.

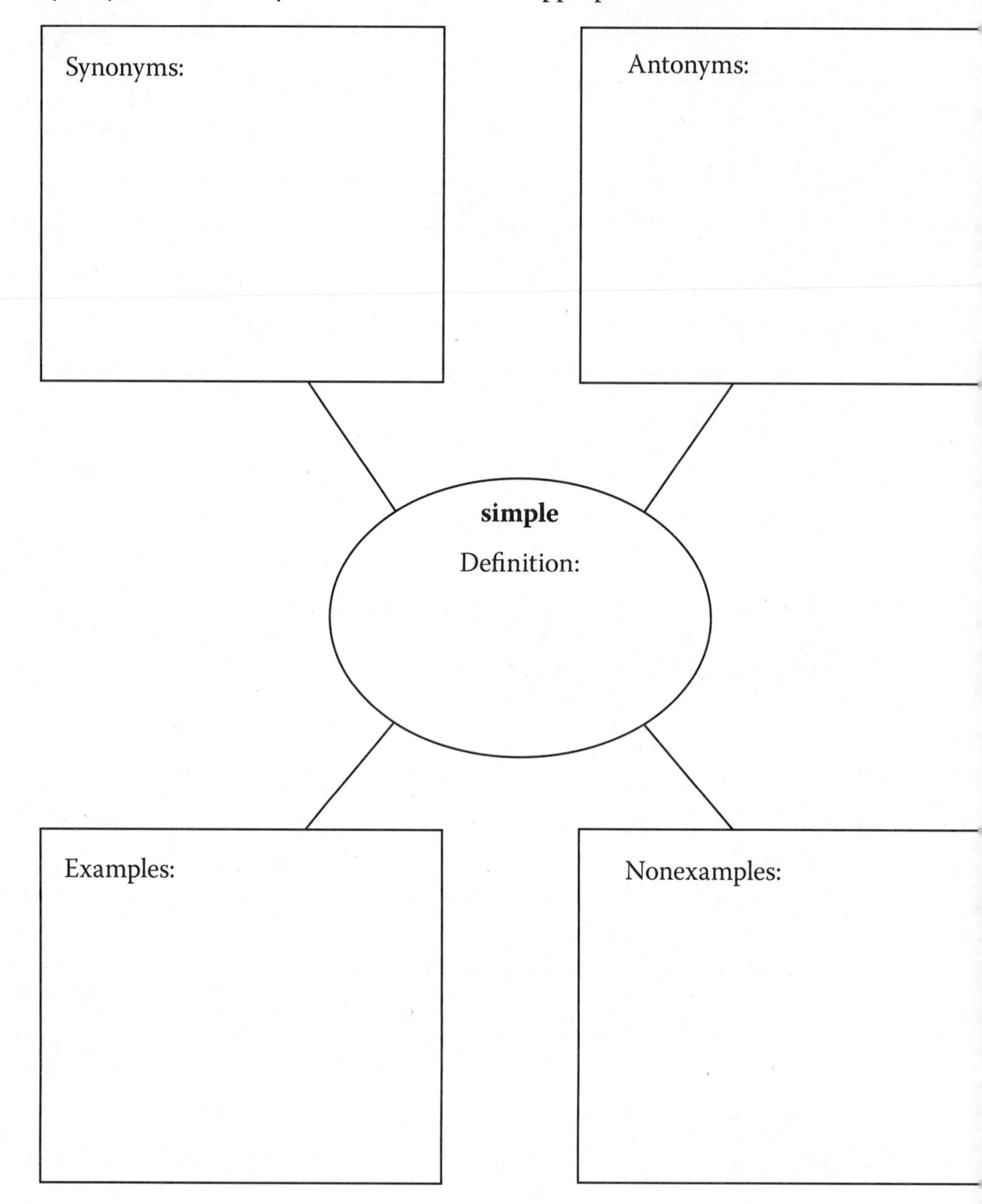

Making Connections

Make connections to the word *culture* by mapping other words related to the word.

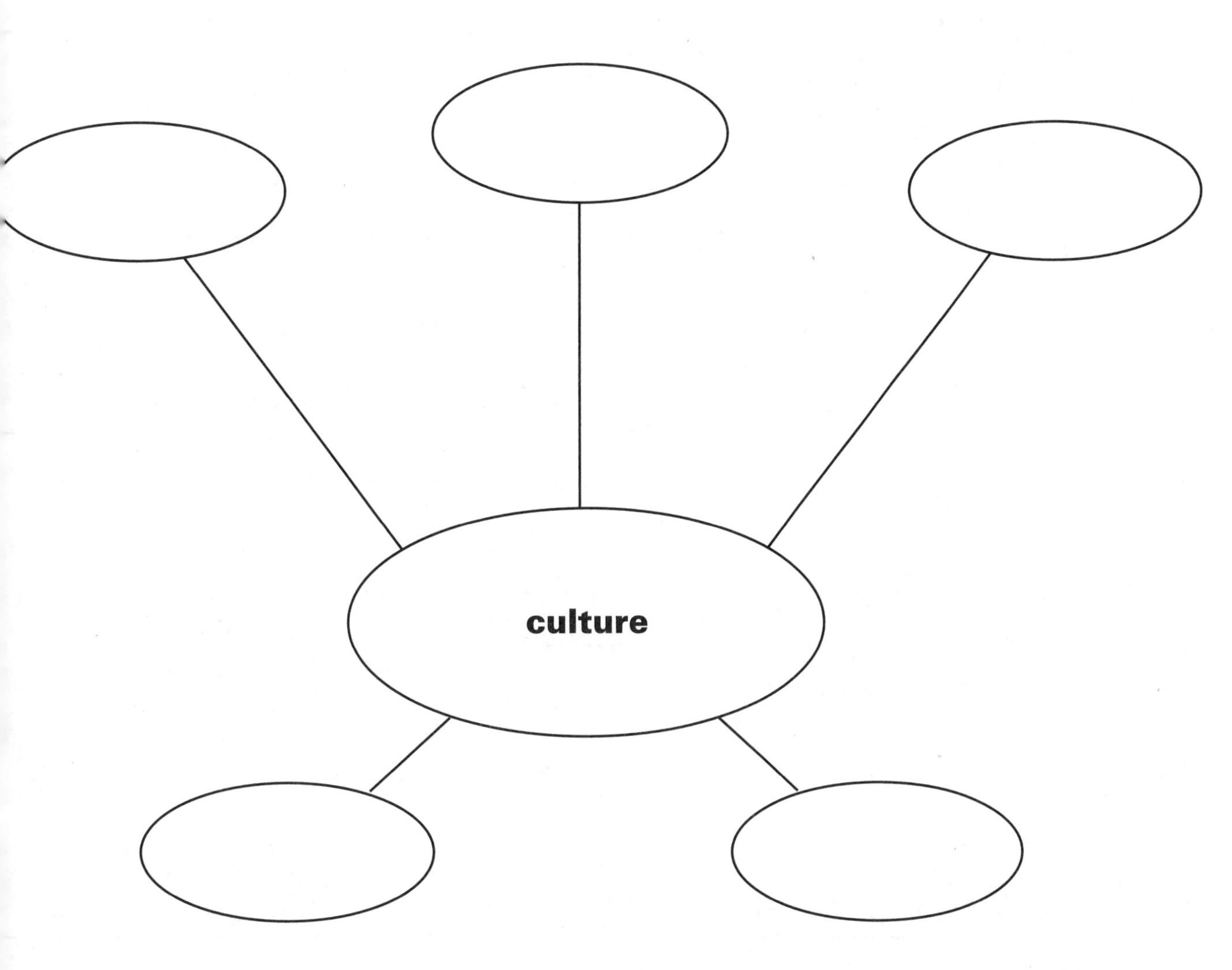

Adverbs and Prepositional Phrases

Read the base sentence and add a predicate painter that answers the *how*, *when*, or *where* question. Move the predicate painter and rewrite the sentence.

1. The band played ____________________.
   (when)

   ____

   ____

2. The twins jog ____________________.
   (where)

   ____

   ____

3. The clock ticks ____________________.
   (how)

   ____

   ____

4. The fans clapped ____________________.
   (when)

   ____

   ____

5. Jazz, rock, and hip-hop were classics ____________________.
   (when)

   ____

   ____

Verb Forms

Verbs signal time, and some verbs show action.

Tense Timeline

A **tense timeline** shows three points in time—past, present, and future.

Yesterday	Today	Tomorrow
Past	Present	Future

Rewrite each present tense sentence to show that it happened in the past. Then, rewrite each sentence to show that it will happen in the future.

Yesterday	Today	Tomorrow
Past	Present	Future
	-s	
He ________________.	He bats.	He ________________.
She ________________.	She jogs.	She ________________.
It ________________.	It rests.	It ________________.

Word Fluency

Read the words fluently.

	Correct	Errors
1st Try		
2nd Try		

socks	fuzz	stuff	fast	yell	puffs	missing	spilled	pass	desk	10
stuff	fast	yell	puffs	missing	spilled	pass	desk	fixed	pulled	20
yell	puffs	missing	spilled	pass	desk	fixed	pulled	telling	off	30
missing	spilled	pass	desk	fixed	pulled	telling	off	gasp	snack	40
pass	desk	fixed	pulled	telling	off	gasp	snack	slots	quick	50
fixed	pulled	telling	off	gasp	snack	slots	quick	deck	boxing	60
telling	off	gasp	snack	slots	quick	deck	boxing	fuzz	socks	70
gasp	snack	slots	quick	deck	boxing	fuzz	socks	fast	stuff	80
slots	quick	deck	boxing	fuzz	socks	fast	stuff	puffs	yell	90
deck	boxing	fuzz	socks	fast	stuff	puffs	yell	spilled	missing	100

Using Two-Column Notes

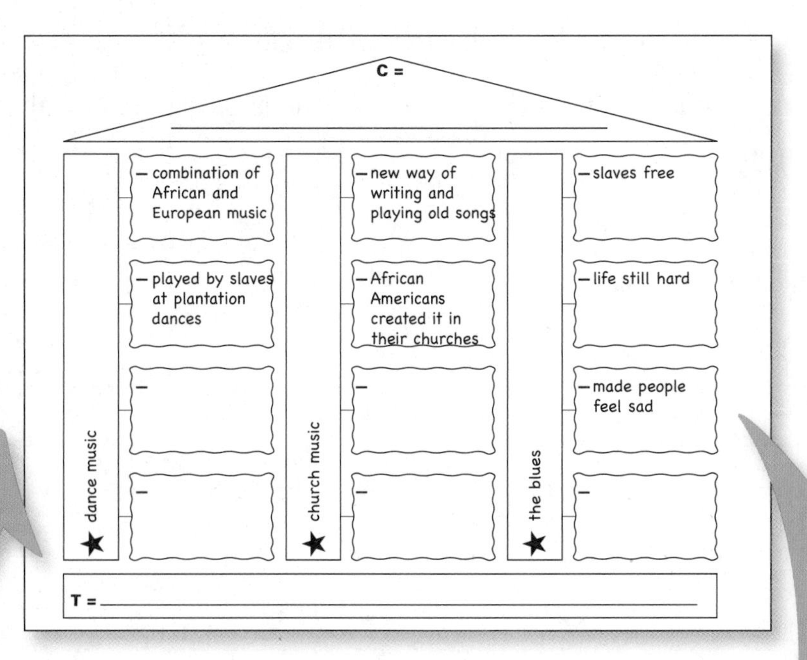

Both graphic organizers can organize the same information.

Informal (Two-Column) Notes

Topic: Foundation	
☆Wall: Supporting Detail	—Window: Elaboration —Window: Elaboration —Window: Elaboration —Window: Elaboration
☆Wall: Supporting Detail	—Window: Elaboration —Window: Elaboration —Window: Elaboration —Window: Elaboration
☆Wall: Supporting Detail	—Window: Elaboration —Window: Elaboration —Window: Elaboration —Window: Elaboration

Prepare to Write: From Prompt to Two-Column Notes

Part A

Read the prompt. Circle the topic. Underline the directions.

Identify three "ingredients," or types of music, in the jazz recipe. Tell about them in a paragraph.

Part B

Turn the prompt into the topic sentence for a paragraph. Write the topic sentence.

___

___

Part C

As you read, take notes on the "ingredients" in jazz music.

Topic:	
☆	— — —
☆	— — —
☆	— — —
☆	— — —
☆	— — —
☆	— — —

Concluding Sentences

Read each topic sentence. Circle the topic in each sentence. Then, use synonyms and changes in word order to create a concluding sentence. Write your new sentence on the lines below the topic sentence.

1. **Topic Sentence:**
   A library is a great place to find new things to enjoy.
   Possible Concluding Sentence: ____________________
   ____
   ____

2. **Topic Sentence:**
   A dancer creates moves to express a song's rhythm and feeling.
   Possible Concluding Sentence: ____________________
   ____
   ____

3. **Topic Sentence:**
   Riding a bike is a healthy, money-saving way to travel.
   Possible Concluding Sentence: ____________________
   ____
   ____

4. **Topic Sentence:**
   If someone gets hurt or lost, a cell phone can be a lifesaver.
   Possible Concluding Sentence: ____________________
   ____
   ____

5. **Topic Sentence:**
   A good breakfast can make the whole day better.
   Possible Concluding Sentence: ____________________
   ____
   ____

Six Traits of Effective Writing

Trait		What does this mean?
	Ideas and Content	Focus on the main ideas or story line. Supporting details (expository) or images/events (narrative) build understanding.
	Organization	Order of ideas and supporting details (expository) or clear beginning, middle, and end (narrative) make sense. Introduction, transitions, and conclusion help keep the reader hooked on the writing.
	Voice and Audience Awareness	Style suits both the audience and purpose of the writing.
	Word Choice	"Just right" words for the topic and audience
	Sentence Fluency	Varied sentence use; no run-on sentences and sentence fragments
Editor's Marks add or change text delete text move text new paragraph capitalize lowercase insert period check spelling or spell out word	**Conventions**	Spelling, punctuation, grammar and usage, capitalization, and indenting paragraphs

Using New Vocabulary

Fill in the blanks with the appropriate vocabulary words. If you need assistance, use the word bank at the bottom of the page.

Jazz music was born in America. It was created over time using a _______________ that started with work songs from ships and fields. Work songs had a _______________ beat that helped pass the time. Next, African Americans _______________ their faith in song by changing the words and beat of church music. Americans sang _______________ ballads that told sad stories about bravery. Though the songs were good, they were not upbeat. There was a _______________ for music that people could dance to. African and European music _______________ to create ballroom dance music. The beat changed again with ragtime music. Tunes were loud and lively. Then frustrated former slaves began to sing the blues about life on and off the _______________ and hard times. Jazz music was made with American ingredients and is enjoyed at many _______________ events.

Word Bank

steady	social	simple	plantations
combined	demand	expressed	recipe

Reading for Fluency

Read the passage with prosody. Chunk the words into phrases and create an image in your head as you read.

Stuck in the Mud

The red van is a mess. It was stuck in the mud. We had fun, but my dad and mom are mad.

My pals Ted and Sam got into my van. I said it is fun to run laps in the mud and ruts by the rocks at the mill. We slid in the ruts and mud. It was fun. There was a fast stop.

The van was stuck. I backed it up just a bit. Ted and Sam pulled and pulled. Ted and Sam huffed and puffed. The van quit backing up. We had no gas, and it was stuck in the muck. What a mess. It was not fun. The clock said six and the red van was stuck. What do we do when it gets past dusk? We are not big buff men. We are just kids. I said, "I will get my dad." Where can I go to call? I said to my pals, "I will jog up to the top of the hill. Dad will get us, but he will be mad and will fuss."

I called Dad. I said, "The van is stuck."

He asked, "Where are you? Are you lost? Are kids with you?"

I said, "I am with Ted and Sam. We are up on the hill by the mill, and there is no gas in the van."

Dad is yelling, but he is not telling Mom yet. He will get us. But, there is not one dab of gas in his rig. He will get gas and get a can for the van as well.

He called Mom and said, "I will pick them up in a bit."

The van is back. Mom is mad and fussing. She said, "There will not be one spot or one speck of mud on the van. It will not still smell of mud. You will wax it. You will fill it with gas. Do you get it?"

Yes, we get it. Here are rags for the van, Sam. Here are suds, Ted. What a mess! That is the last of the fun in the mud for us.

Sentence Four-Square

Determine synonyms for the words in the sentence. Then, write three sentences that restate the ideas in the model sentence.

Everyone in our class likes listening to music. **Synonyms** everyone: ____________________ ____________________ likes: ____________________ listening: ____________________ music: ____________________	Sentence 1 ____________________ ____________________ ____________________ Sentence 2 ____________________ ____________________ ____________________ Sentence 3 ____________________ ____________________ ____________________

Many varieties of music inspire teens. **Synonyms** many: ____________________ ____________________ varieties: ____________________ inspire: ____________________ ____________________ teens: ____________________ ____________________	Sentence 1 ____________________ ____________________ ____________________ Sentence 2 ____________________ ____________________ ____________________ Sentence 3 ____________________ ____________________ ____________________

Answering Questions

Listen to the prompts and possible answers. Fill in the bubble for your answer choice.

Example: When did the blues begin to be played?

To answer this question, I need to include _____.

Ⓐ a general location or specific place
Ⓑ a reason or explanation
Ⓒ a specific time, date, or event
Ⓓ the way something is done

1. Where was the banjo invented?

To answer this question, I need to include _____.

Ⓐ a specific time, date, or event
Ⓑ a reason or explanation
Ⓒ a general location or specific place
Ⓓ the way something is done

2. Why did people play the blues?

To answer this question, I need to include _____.

Ⓐ a reason or explanation
Ⓑ a specific time, date, or event
Ⓒ a general location or specific place
Ⓓ the way something is done

3. How do you play the trumpet?

To answer this question, I need to include _____.

Ⓐ a reason or explanation
Ⓑ a general location or specific place
Ⓒ the way something is done
Ⓓ a specific time, date, or event

4. When did New Orleans become a center for jazz?

To answer this question, I need to include _____.

Ⓐ a reason or explanation
Ⓑ a general location or specific place
Ⓒ the way something is done
Ⓓ a specific time, date, or event

5. Who invented dance music?

To answer this question, I need to include _____.

Ⓐ information about a person or grou
Ⓑ a specific time, date, or event
Ⓒ a general location or specific place
Ⓓ a reason or explanation

Adverbs and Adverbial Phrases

Listen to the prompts and possible answers. Fill in the bubble for your answer choice.

Example: Choose the adverb or adverbial phrase in the following sentence:

After the game, the winning team yelled a cheer.

- Ⓐ the winning team
- Ⓑ yelled
- Ⓒ After the game
- Ⓓ a cheer

1. Choose the adverb or adverbial phrase in the following sentence:

   My friend gave me the library book in the hall.

   - Ⓐ in the hall
   - Ⓑ the library book
   - Ⓒ gave me
   - Ⓓ My friend

2. Choose the adverb or adverbial phrase in the following sentence:

   The Fourth of July fireworks exploded with a loud bang.

   - Ⓐ The Fourth of July
   - Ⓑ exploded
   - Ⓒ fireworks
   - Ⓓ with a loud bang

3. Choose the adverb or adverbial phrase in the following sentence:

   The yellow flowers bloomed early.

   - Ⓐ early
   - Ⓑ bloomed
   - Ⓒ flowers
   - Ⓓ yellow

4. Choose the adverb or adverbial phrase in the following sentence:

   The yellow cat sat and waited on the steps.

   - Ⓐ and waited
   - Ⓑ The yellow cat
   - Ⓒ sat
   - Ⓓ on the steps

5. Choose the adverb or adverbial phrase in the following sentence:

   The mother hen clucked loudly.

   - Ⓐ hen
   - Ⓑ The mother
   - Ⓒ loudly
   - Ⓓ clucked

Nonexamples

Listen to the questions and possible answers. Fill in the bubble for your answer choice.

Example: Which word is a nonexample of *ball game*?

- Ⓐ baseball
- Ⓑ swimming
- Ⓒ football
- Ⓓ basketball

1. Which word is a nonexample of *heavy*?
   - Ⓐ rock
   - Ⓑ schoolbooks
   - Ⓒ feather
   - Ⓓ elephant

2. Which word is a nonexample of *dish*?
   - Ⓐ knife
   - Ⓑ plate
   - Ⓒ bowl
   - Ⓓ cup

3. Which word is a nonexample of *wet*?
   - Ⓐ ocean
   - Ⓑ desert
   - Ⓒ lake
   - Ⓓ puddle

4. Which word is a nonexample of *yellow*?
   - Ⓐ strawberry
   - Ⓑ sun
   - Ⓒ sunflower
   - Ⓓ banana

5. Which word is a nonexample of *young*?
   - Ⓐ baby
   - Ⓑ seedling
   - Ⓒ chick
   - Ⓓ grandmother

Let's Focus: "Coming Clean About Toxic Pollution"

Content Focus
toxic pollution

Type of Text
informational

Author's Purpose: ______________________________

Big Ideas
Consider these Big Idea questions. Write your answer for each question.

How does toxic waste pollute air, land, and water?

____

____

How can we help prevent toxins from harming plants, animals, and people?

____

____

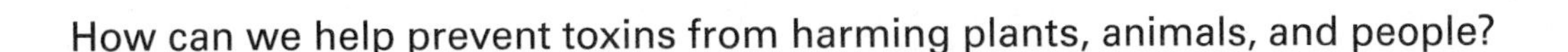

Informational Preview Checklist: "Coming Clean About Toxic Pollution" on pages 163–165.

- ☐ Title: What clue does it provide about the passage?
- ☐ Pictures and Captions: What additional information is added here?
- ☐ Headings: What topics will this text include?
- ☐ Margin Information: What vocabulary is important to understand in this text?
- ☐ Maps, Charts, Graphs: Are additional visuals present that will help me understand?

Reading for a Purpose

1. How does toxic waste spoil everything?
2. What are the results of air pollution?
3. What is smog and how is it made?
4. How does acid rain harm the environment?
5. Where do toxins come from?
6. How can we prevent land pollution?
7. Why does the author say "It's time to come clean about toxic pollution"?

Key Passage Vocabulary: "Coming Clean About Toxic Pollution"

Rate your knowledge of the words. Define the words. Draw a picture to help you remember the definition.

Vocabulary	Knowledge Rating	Definition	Picture
spoil	0 1 2 3		
destroy	0 1 2 3		
substance	0 1 2 3		
pollution	0 1 2 3		
modern	0 1 2 3		
device	0 1 2 3		
variety	0 1 2 3		
support	0 1 2 3		

Coming Clean About Toxic Pollution

Toxic Waste

Toxic waste **spoils** everything. It **destroys** our land, water, air, plants, and animals. A toxic **substance**, even a small amount, can harm plant or animal life. Where does toxic waste come from? It can come from factories that make a wide range of products. It can come from pesticides sprayed on the land. When we throw things away, toxic substances get buried in our landfills. When it rains, toxic pollutants in the ground are washed into rivers, lakes, and oceans. How do these toxins impact our environment?

Air Pollution

Toxins impact the quality of our air. Air supplies the oxygen we need. When toxic substances fill the air, we breathe them into our lungs. When the air is polluted, we breathe in harmful gases and fumes. We breathe in poison! We can't always see the **pollution**. Sometimes, we see it as a dirty mist called smog. Household products like lighter fluid and aerosol sprays contribute to smog. The fumes that come from cars and trucks also make smog. Most **modern** cars have a **device** called a catalytic converter. This device treats the exhaust before the fumes leave the car, removing harmful substances. What can we do to help? Make simple changes in our daily lives. Avoid using lighter fluid. Replace aerosol deodorant and hairspray with solids, gels, or liquids.

spoil
to harm or damage something

destroy
to damage, ruin, or harm beyond repair

substance
what something is made from

pollution
the waste or poisonous substances put into the air, water, or land

modern
having to do with present time

device
a machine or tool that has a special use

Emissions from power plants react with sunlight and moisture to create acid rain.

Land Pollution

Our land is also negatively impacted by toxins. In the 1960s, the average person created approximately 2.7 pounds of garbage each day. By 2007, that number had almost doubled to 4.6 pounds of garbage each day. 30 Where does all of this garbage go every day? Most of it goes into landfills where toxic substances can seep into the soil. Pesticides and fertilizers used by farmers can also soak into the land, causing pollution. Poisons in the ground are absorbed by plants and any creature 35 that eats the plants. What can we do to help? Create less garbage by recycling. Drink water from the faucet instead of in plastic bottles. Look for foods grown without pesticides.

Acid Rain

Acid rain illustrates how pollution spreads and 40 impacts all aspects of the environment. When air pollution combines with water in the air, acid rain is created. Gases that come from vehicles and power plants pollute the air, making acid rain possible. Wherever acid rain falls, it damages the environment. 45 It can kill plants on land as well as creatures in lakes and streams. It is corrosive enough to damage stone structures. It eats away at stone, causing permanent damage to buildings and statues. What can we do to help? We can drive more fuel-efficient cars and reduce 50 our energy consumption.

River Pollution

Pollution threatens all of our water resources. There are many toxins in our homes. These include paint thinner, cleaning supplies, bug spray, and fertilizer.

When toxins are washed down the drain, they get into
55 our sewers and eventually our rivers. If these toxins are buried in landfills, the rain can flush them into rivers. There, they harm the fish and other forms of life. What can we do to help? We can limit our use of water and discard household chemicals safely.

Dead Lakes

60 Our lakes are also damaged by pollution. It disturbs the balance between a **variety** of plants and living creatures. Pollution falls or seeps into the lake. Different types of pollution can make water plants like algae grow rapidly. The algae block the sunlight and
65 use up all the water's oxygen. All living organisms in the lake, including fish, die. The lake is dead. A dead lake cannot **support** life. The animals that relied on the lake for food are also at risk. What can we do to help? We can remember that polluting the land means
70 polluting the water! Stopping the litter that enters our lakes can make a difference.

variety
a number of different kinds or types

support
to have what is needed to maintain or keep something going

Ocean Pollution

In addition to polluting lakes and rivers, many of the toxic substances produced on land end up in our oceans. When waste pours into the sea, it may be
75 eaten by small fish. When bigger fish and sea animals eat those fish, the toxins build up to dangerous levels. Mercury impacted tuna in this way. As creatures poisoned with mercury were eaten by other animals, the mercury levels rose to unsafe levels. Eventually, the
80 mercury levels found in tuna made them unsafe for humans to eat. The effects of pollution on sea life and shore wildlife can be terrible. We cannot think of the ocean as a place to dump our waste. What can we do to help? Recycle and dispose of our trash responsibly. Get
85 rid of pet waste properly so that it doesn't contaminate our water sources. Pick up after your dog. Flush the waste down the toilet or double wrap it and throw it in the trash. Composting the waste makes it safe and fertilizes your yard at the same time!

Your Responsibility

90 It's time to come clean about toxic pollution. Many industries pollute, but so do individuals. People drive cars, create waste, and litter. All of these actions have a negative impact on our environment. We all need to do our part to protect our air, land, and water from toxic
95 waste. What else can you do to help?

Multiple-Meaning Map

Determine the meanings of the word *plant*. Write the definitions in the boxes. Use the word in a sentence on the lines below the boxes.

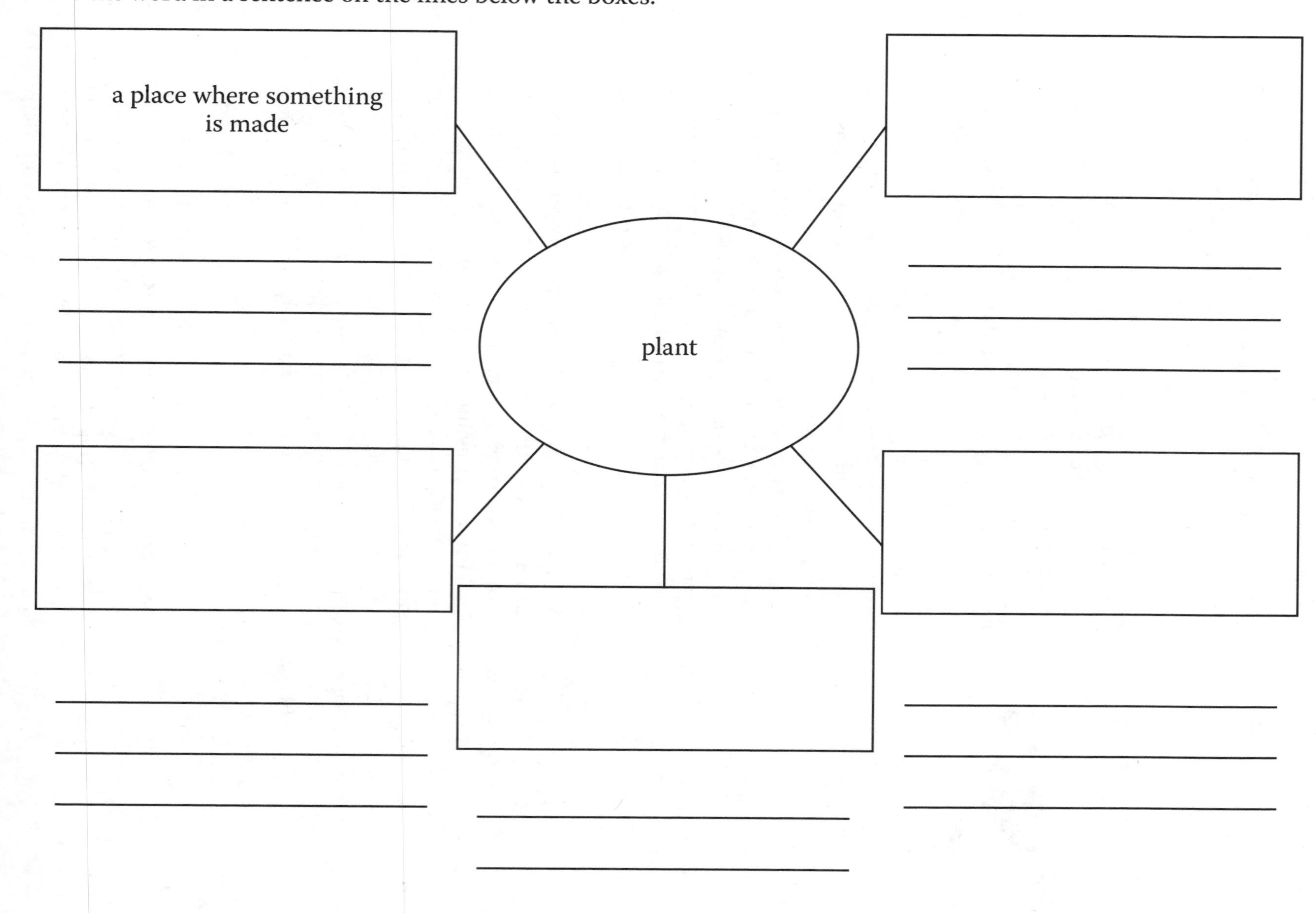

The Verb *be*

- ***Am***, ***is***, and ***are*** are all present tense forms of the verb ***be***.
- Forms of ***be*** can be used as helping verbs.
- Different forms of ***be*** are used with different personal pronouns to achieve subject-verb agreement in sentences.

Correct Use of Present Tense Forms of *Be*		
Person	**Singular**	**Plural**
First Person	I **am**	we **are**
Second Person	you **are**	you **are**
Third Person	he (she, it) **is**	they **are**

Function: Helping Verb

Add ***-ing*** to the verb and use the helping verb ***am***, ***is***, or ***are*** in front of the verb to show action happening right now. This form of present tense is called ***present progressive***.

Person	Singular	Plural
First Person	I am sitting.	We are sitting.
Second Person	You are sitting.	You are sitting.
Third Person	He (She, It) is sitting.	They are sitting.

Forms of the Verb *be*

Part A

Write the correct form of *be* on the line. Circle the subject. Identify whether the subject is singular or plural. Write *singular* or *plural* on the line.

1. Kelly and Sam ____________ below the window. ________________
2. Jess, Dan, and I ____________ behind the curtains. ________________
3. We ____________ at the mall. ________________
4. They ____________ on the mat. ________________
5. The dog ____________ under the table. ________________
6. She ____________ at the beach. ________________
7. You ____________ in my chair. ________________
8. I ____________ on my way. ________________
9. Sam ____________ at the bank. ________________

Part B

Change the underlined verb in each sentence to present progressive.

Present Tense	Present Progressive Tense
Examples: I <u>grill</u> fish. The men <u>lift</u> the table.	**Examples:** I am grilling fish. The men are lifting the table.
1. The cops <u>block</u> traffic. 2. I <u>kick</u> rocks off the dock. 3. Scott <u>rocks</u> to the jazz. 4. Lon-Ban <u>plants</u> yams. 5. The dog <u>sniffs</u> the trash.	1. The cops ________________ traffic. 2. I ________________ rocks off the dock. 3. Scott ________________ to the jazz. 4. Lon-Ban ________________ yams. 5. The dog ________________ the trash.

Tense Timeline

Sort the following verbs and verb phrases according to their tenses. All verbs are past or present tense.

jump	blocked	fills	is batting
is filling	jumped	bats	filled
batted	is jumping	blocks	are blocking

Past (has already happened)	Present (is happening)	Future (has not happened yet)

Descriptive Writing

Sensory word choice is the key to descriptive writing. Word choice and the use of comparisons help the reader or listener create an image of what is being described. When writing descriptive compositions, ask the following questions:

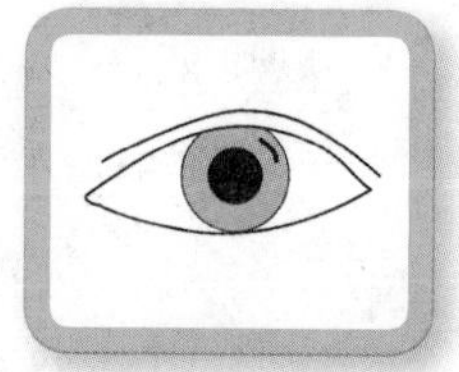

What do you want the reader to **see**?

Hints: colors; shapes; weather; expressions on faces; gestures; people doing things alone or with others; objects; natural features

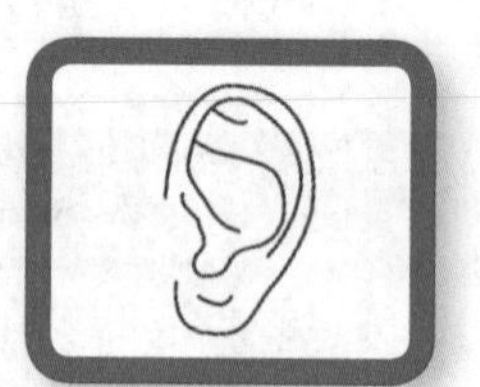

What do you want the reader to **hear**?

Hints: volume, tone, and expression of people's voices; music; rain; wind; trains; airplanes; traffic; animal sounds

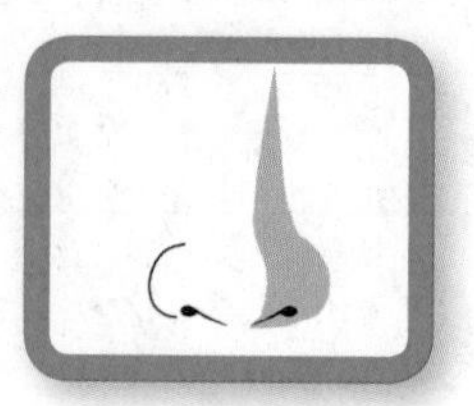

What do you want the reader to **smell**?

Hints: flowers and trees; perfume; food; smoke; exhaust; rain

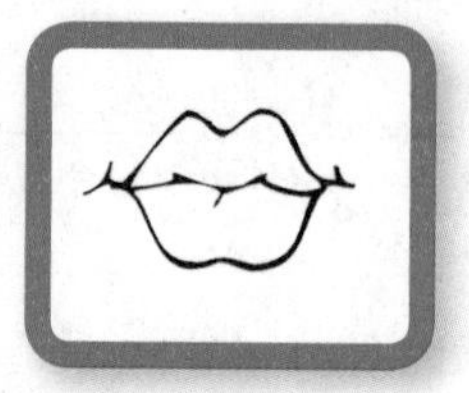

What do you want the reader to **taste**?

Hints: food or drink that is sweet, sour, salty, or bitter

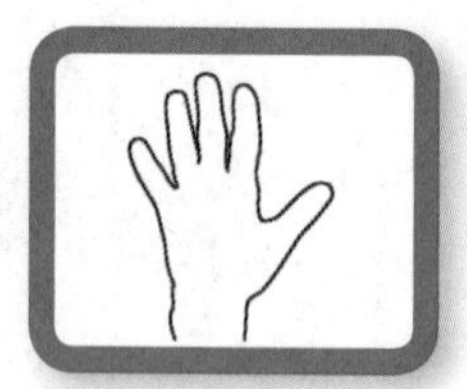

What do you want the reader to **feel**?

Hints: surfaces of different temperatures and textures; liquids of different types and forms

Word Fluency

Read the words fluently.

	Correct	Errors
1st Try		
2nd Try		

smoke	rule	stuck	mask	eve	slush	stick	bikes	tube	let	10
stuck	mask	eve	slush	stick	bikes	tube	let	quite	cute	20
eve	slush	stick	bikes	tube	let	quite	cute	shell	locked	30
stick	bikes	tube	let	quite	cute	shell	locked	shake	shale	40
tube	let	quite	cute	shell	locked	shake	shale	doll	sniffing	50
quite	cute	shell	locked	shake	shale	doll	sniffing	less	quote	60
shell	locked	shake	shale	doll	sniffing	less	quote	rule	smoke	70
shake	shale	doll	sniffing	less	quote	rule	smoke	mask	stuck	80
doll	sniffing	less	quote	rule	smoke	mask	stuck	slush	eve	90
less	quote	rule	smoke	mask	stuck	slush	eve	bikes	tube	100

Related Words

Using the base word *cycle,* create words by adding prefixes and suffixes. Write the new words on the lines.

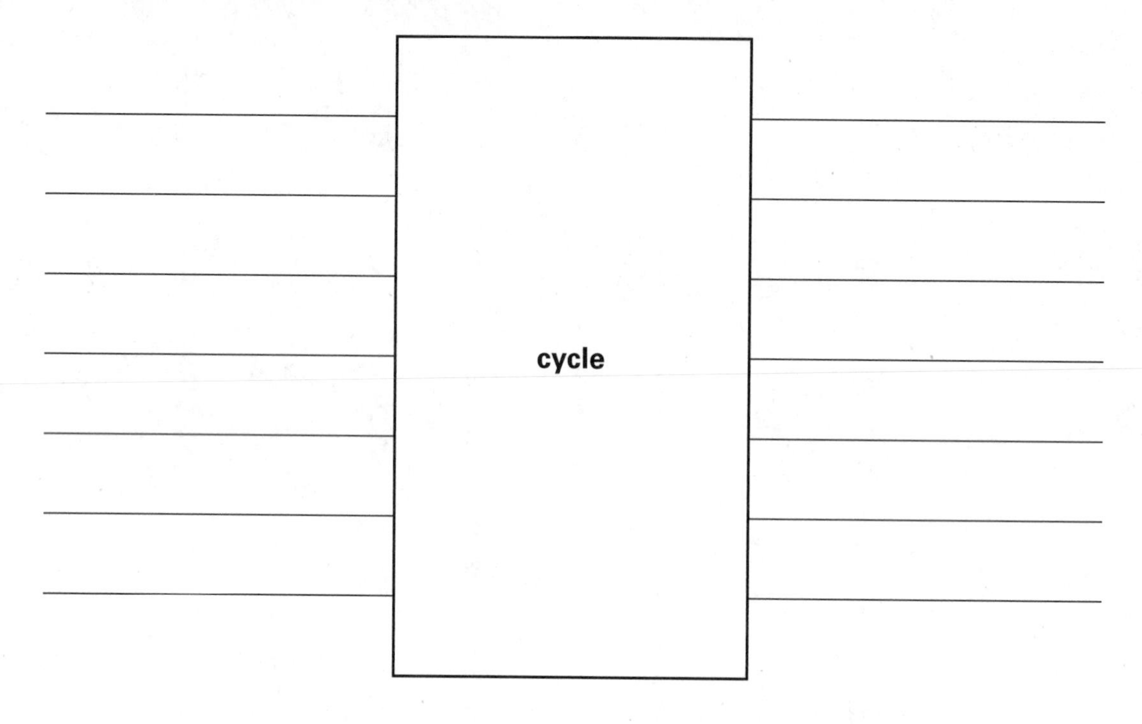

Adjectives

Adjectives describe nouns.

They answer:

- *How many?*
- *What kind?*
- *Which one?*

Some prepositional phrases act like adjectives because they can also tell about attributes of a noun. These phrases begin with a preposition and end with a noun.

The subject of the sentence can have adjectives and prepositional phrases that act as adjectives describing the person, place, or thing that the sentence is about.

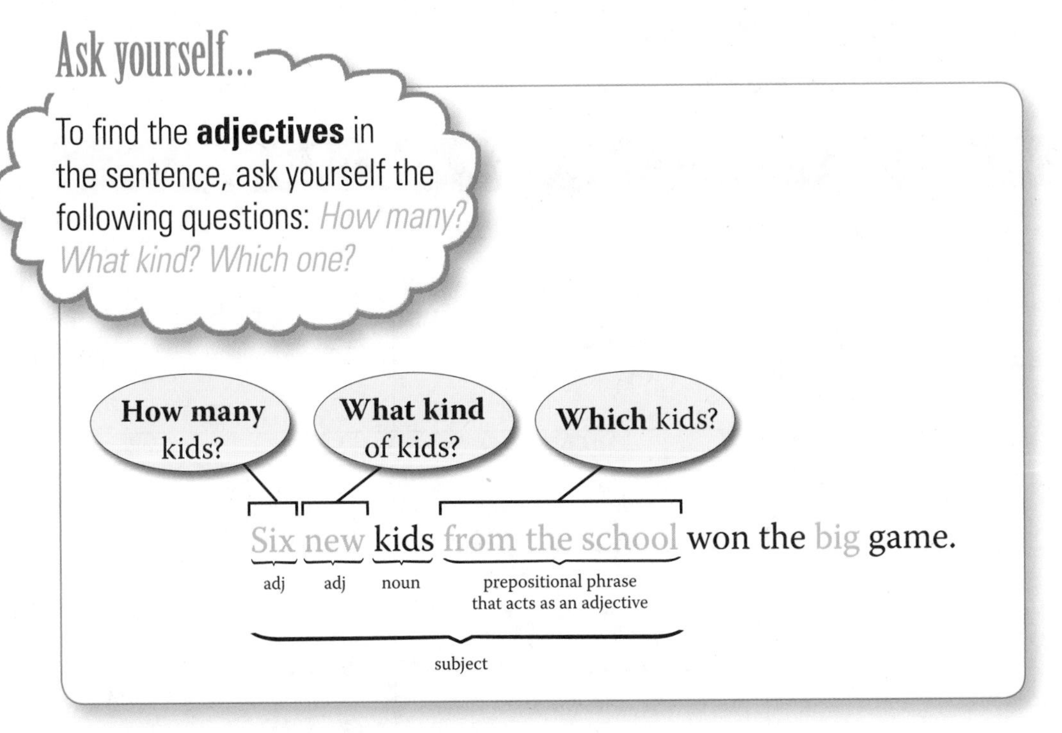

Adjectives can also describe other nouns in the sentence.

What kind of game? big

Sort It: *Which One? How Many?* or *What Kind?*

Read each sentence. Determine what question the underlined adjective answers and write it in the correct column.

1. The hot wax is dripping on the mat.
2. The brisk air was polluted.
3. That bobcat hid in the cabin.
4. The cab with the flat stopped traffic.
5. Six frogs were in the lab.
6. The crabs were digging in the damp sand.
7. Many toxins pollute the air.
8. Gas mist from vans and cabs clogs the environment.
9. The colorful quilt was a gift for her.
10. The toxic plant made them sick.

Which one?	How many?	What kind?

Critical Understandings: Direction Words

Read the information in the chart.

	Prompt If the prompt asks you to . . .	How to Respond The response requires you to . . .	Model For example . . .
Recall	Define	tell or write the meaning or definition	**Define** the unknown word using a dictionary as a reference.
	List	state a series of names, ideas, or events	**List** key details from the text that support the main idea.
	Name	label specific information	**Name** the book that was published in 2008.
	State	say or write specific information	**State** the meaning of the title.
	Tell	say or write specific information	**Tell** the date that the book was published.
	Use	apply information or a procedure	**Use** text features to identify the topic of the text.
Conceptual Understanding	Categorize	create groups and place information into those groups based on shared characteristics	**Categorize** different types of mammals.
	Compare	state the similarities between two or more things	**Compare** whales and dolphins.
	Describe	state detailed information about a topic	**Describe** the relationship between the two topics.
	Explain	express understanding of an idea or concept	**Explain** how the major event impacted the situation.
	Infer	provide a logical conclusion using evidence and prior knowledge	Use the information in the text to **infer** the reason for the celebration.
	Interpret	make sense of or assign meaning to something	**Interpret** information from the text and the chart to explain the topic.
	Relate	explain the relationship between ideas or concepts	**Relate** whale songs to bird songs.
	Show	demonstrate understanding of information	Use the timeline to **show** how opinions have changed.
	Summarize	tell the most important ideas or concepts	**Summarize** the key details of the passage.

Critical Understandings

Read the prompts at the bottom of the page. Then, read the passage and respond to the prompts.

Rachel Carson

Rachel Carson's love of nature changed the world. Her book *Silent Spring* was published in 1962. What did the title mean? It predicted a terrible time. The book opened with a description of a beautiful town. When a fine, white powder was sprayed from the sky, the town fell silent. There were no birds singing. Carson warned that people should not try to control nature. Carson said that trying to have nature work for us could lead to trouble. We didn't know what could happen in the future. She said that the destruction of any part of the web of life could threaten the human race. Carson said, "We need to think of ourselves differently. The universe is vast. It is incredible. We are just a tiny part of it."

Fast Facts

Born: May 27, 1907, in Springdale, Pennsylvania

Died: April 14, 1964, in Silver Spring, Maryland

Books: *Under the Sea-Wind* (1941), *The Sea Around Us* (1951), *The Edge of the Sea* (1955), *Silent Spring* (1962), and *The Sense of Wonder* (posthumous, 1965)

1. **Tell** what Carson said could threaten the human race.

___

___

___

2. **Name** Carson's book that changed the world.

___

___

Critical Understandings (*cont.*)

3. **List** the books written by Rachel Carson.

4. **Define** *posthumous*, using context. **Use** a dictionary to confirm your definition.

5. **State** Carson's warning from *Silent Spring.*

Phrase Fluency

Read each phrase fluently.

	Errors	Correct
1st Try		
2nd Try		

Phrase		Phrase	
Luke and Duke's pal	4	spelled his name	82
he kicks	6	the slate rock	85
Jake's five mice	9	are filling cages	88
which tame apes	12	have packed	90
the cute kid	15	likes to ride	93
we have pulled	18	on this long rope	97
Jane's and June's pal	22	packed his bags	100
your in-line skates	25	make a mess	103
the dim hole	28	was buzzing	105
this hot pig	31	ate rice cakes	108
she likes	33	where she lives	111
with my mom	36	from the cage	114
am tacking the pin	40	made of slate	117
on the deck	43	you can	119
the six bones	46	she waves	121
were smelling it	49	said to his wife	125
it makes	51	do you see	128
the ripe lime	54	just one time	131
as fast as she can	59	his best game	134
do you have	62	in our home	137
gives his best	65	I have passed	140
into the gate	68	by the dig site	144
is packing them	71	the lame male	147
to the red pole	75	my dad's job	150
be at the game	79	willing to tell	153

Phrase Dictation: Adjectives and Inflectional Endings

Part A

Listen to the phrase and repeat it. Write it in the chart. If the phrase contains an adjective, underline it and write it in the proper column. If the phrase contains a verb with an inflectional ending, circle it and write it in the proper column.

Phrase	Adjective	Verb: Inflectional Ending
1.		
2.		
3.		
4.		
5.		

Part B

Use the phrases to complete the following sentences:

1. The men ______________________________ with food.
2. ______________________________ live in a cage in his room.
3. Sam ______________________________ carefully.
4. I ______________________________ on the board.
5. ______________________________ has dark green skin and has a nice smell.

Critical Understandings

Preread the prompts. Then, read the passage and respond to the prompts.

Rachel Carson's love of nature changed the world. Her book *Silent Spring* was published in 1962. What did the title mean? It predicted a terrible time. The book opened with a description of a beautiful town. When a fine, white powder was sprayed from the sky, the town fell silent. There were no birds singing. Carson warned that people should not try to control nature. Carson said that trying to have nature work for us could lead to trouble. We didn't know what could happen in the future. She said that the destruction of any part of the web of life could threaten the human race. Carson said, "We need to think of ourselves differently. The universe is vast. It is incredible. We are just a tiny part of it."

Fast Facts

Born:	May 27, 1907, in Springdale, Pennsylvania
Died:	April 14, 1964, in Silver Spring, Maryland
Books:	*Under the Sea-Wind* (1941), *The Sea Around Us* (1951), *The Edge of the Sea* (1955), *Silent Spring* (1962), and *The Sense of Wonder* (posthumous, 1965)

1. **List** two states where Carson lived.

____

____

2. **Tell** the date when Carson's first book was published.

____

____

3. **State** the reason that the birds stopped singing in *Silent Spring.*

____

____

4. **Use** context to **define** *vast.*

____

5. **Use** the chart to **name** the book published after Carson died.

____

____

Ask and Answer Questions

Read "Coming Clean About Toxic Pollution." After each section, write a question or prompt for your partner to respond to using the question words on page 14 or the direction words on page 175.

Toxic Waste *Where?* *Name*

1. ______________________________

____

Air Pollution *What?* *State*

2. ______________________________

____

Land Pollution *Who?* *Tell*

3. ______________________________

____

Acid Rain *How?* *Use*

4. ______________________________

____

River Pollution *Where?* *List*

5. ______________________________

____

Dead Lakes *Why?* *State*

6. ______________________________

____

Ocean Pollution/Your Responsibility *What?* *Tell*

7. ______________________________

____

Six Traits of Writing: Responding to Questions

Trait		Questions to Ask Myself	Comments from Peer Editor/Teacher
	Ideas and Content	Did I answer the question correctly, focus on the topic, and avoid irrelevant information?	
	Organization	Did I use part of the question in my answer?	
	Word Choice	Did I use my own words, including unit vocabulary words when possible?	
	Sentence Fluency	Did I write a complete sentence that flows without interfering with meaning?	
Editor's Marks: ^ add or change text; delete text; move text; new paragraph; capitalize; / lowercase; insert period; check spelling or spell out word	**Conventions**	Did I use correct capitalization, punctuation, grammar, and spelling?	

Passage Comprehension

Underline the direction word in each question. Then, respond to each prompt using a complete sentence. Write the evidence from the text.

1. State how toxic waste spoils everything.

____

____

____

____

Text Evidence: ____

____

____

____

____

____

____

____

____

2. List three results of air pollution.

- ____
- ____
- ____

Text Evidence: ____

____

____

____

____

Passage Comprehension (*cont.*)

3. Define smog. Include text examples of how smog is made.

Text Evidence:

4. Use information gained from the text and the picture on page 164 to demonstrate understanding of how acid rain harms the environment.

Text Evidence:

5. Tell where toxins come from.

Passage Comprehension (*cont.*)

Text Evidence: ____

____

____

____

____

____

____

____

____

6. Name one of the author's suggestions for preventing land pollution.

____

____

____

____

____

Text Evidence: ____

____

____

____

7. Use context to explain why the author says: "It's time to come clean about toxic pollution."

____

____

____

____

Spelling

Write the words your teacher dictates.

1. ____________
2. ____________
3. ____________
4. ____________
5. ____________
6. ____________
7. ____________
8. ____________
9. ____________
10. ____________
11. ____________
12. ____________

Define It

Determine the category and attributes of each word. Then, write the definition.

Word		Category		Attributes
smog	=		+	

Definition: ______________________________

____

Word		Category		Attributes
oxygen	=		+	

Definition: ______________________________

____

Word		Category		Attributes
pesticide	=		+	

Definition: ______________________________

____

Word		Category		Attributes
waste	=		+	

Definition: ______________________________

____

Attributes

Thinking about the attributes of an object can change our mental picture and help us build connections to other words. Use attributes to complete the chart.

Word	Size	Color	Shape	Parts
fish				
bike				
cake				

Attributes (*cont.*)

Function/Purpose	Touch/Texture	Taste	Sound	Smell

Masterpiece Sentences: Stage 4

Use the picture to answer the questions and write a descriptive sentence.

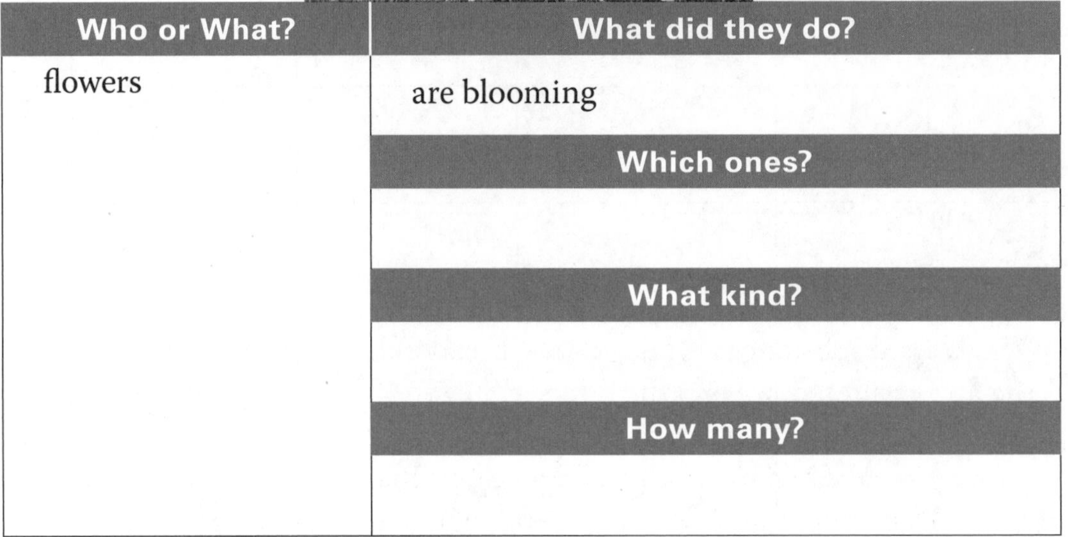

Who or What?	What did they do?
flowers	are blooming
	Which ones?
	What kind?
	How many?

Write your sentence:

____

____

Close Reading: Guided Highlighting

Read the text and complete the tasks.

Coming Clean About Toxic Pollution

Toxic Waste

Toxic waste **spoils** everything. It **destroys** our land, water, air, plants, and animals. A toxic **substance**, even a small amount, can harm plant or animal life. Where does toxic waste come from? It can come from factories that make a wide range of products. It can come from pesticides 5 sprayed on the land. When we throw things away, toxic substances get buried in our landfills. When it rains, toxic pollutants in the ground are washed into rivers, lakes, and oceans. How do these toxins impact our environment?

- **Write an IVF topic sentence for this section.**

____

____

____

Air Pollution

Toxins impact the quality of our air. Air supplies the oxygen we need. 10 When toxic substances fill the air, we breathe them into our lungs. When the air is polluted, we breathe in harmful gases and fumes. We breathe in poison! We can't always see the **pollution**. Sometimes, we see it as a dirty mist called smog. Household products like lighter fluid and aerosol sprays contribute to smog. The fumes that come from cars and trucks also 15 make smog. Most **modern** cars have a **device** called a catalytic converter. This device treats the exhaust before the fumes leave the car, removing harmful substances. What can we do to help? Make simple changes in our daily lives. Avoid using lighter fluid. Replace aerosol deodorant and hairspray with solids, gels, or liquids.

- **Write an IVF topic sentence for this section.**

____

____

____

Close Reading: Guided Highlighting (*cont.*)

Land Pollution

20 Our land is also negatively impacted by toxins. In the 1960s, the average person created approximately 2.7 pounds of garbage each day. By 2007, that number had almost doubled to 4.6 pounds of garbage each day. Where does all of this garbage go every day? Most of it goes into landfills where toxic substances can seep into the soil. Pesticides and fertilizers 25 used by farmers can also soak into the land, causing pollution. Poisons in the ground are absorbed by plants and any creature that eats the plants. What can we do to help? Create less garbage by recycling. Drink water from the faucet instead of in plastic bottles. Look for foods grown without pesticides.

- **Write an IVF topic sentence for this section.**

___

___

___

Acid Rain

30 Acid rain illustrates how pollution spreads and impacts all aspects of the environment. When air pollution combines with water in the air, acid rain is created. Gases that come from vehicles and power plants pollute the air, making acid rain possible. Wherever acid rain falls, it damages the environment. It can kill plants on land as well as creatures in lakes 35 and streams. It is corrosive enough to damage stone structures. It eats away at stone, causing permanent damage to buildings and statues. What can we do to help? We can drive more fuel-efficient cars and reduce our energy consumption.

- **Write an IVF topic sentence for this section.**

___

___

___

Close Reading: Guided Highlighting (*cont.*)

River Pollution

Pollution threatens all of our water resources. There are many toxins in our homes. These include paint thinner, cleaning supplies, bug spray, and fertilizer. When toxins are washed down the drain, they get into our sewers and eventually our rivers. If these toxins are buried in landfills, the rain can flush them into rivers. There, they harm the fish and other forms of life. What can we do to help? We can limit our use of water and discard household chemicals safely.

- **Write an IVF topic sentence for this section.**

____

____

____

Dead Lakes

Our lakes are also damaged by pollution. It disturbs the balance between a **variety** of plants and living creatures. Pollution falls or seeps into the lake. Different types of pollution can make water plants like algae grow rapidly. The algae block the sunlight and use up all the water's oxygen. All living organisms in the lake, including fish, die. The lake is dead. A dead lake cannot **support** life. The animals that relied on the lake for food are also at risk. What can we do to help? We can remember that polluting the land means polluting the water! Stopping the litter that enters our lakes can make a difference.

- **Write an IVF topic sentence for this section.**

____

____

____

Close Reading: Guided Highlighting (*cont.*)

Ocean Pollution

55 In addition to polluting lakes and rivers, many of the toxic substances produced on land end up in our oceans. When waste pours into the sea, it may be eaten by small fish. When bigger fish and sea animals eat those fish, the toxins build up to dangerous levels. Mercury impacted tuna in this way. As creatures poisoned with mercury were eaten by other animals, the 60 mercury levels rose to unsafe levels. Eventually, the mercury levels found in tuna made them unsafe for humans to eat. The effects of pollution on sea life and shore wildlife can be terrible. We cannot think of the ocean as a place to dump our waste. What can we do to help? Recycle and dispose of our trash responsibly. Get rid of pet waste properly so that it doesn't 65 contaminate our water sources. Pick up after your dog. Flush the waste down the toilet or double wrap it and throw it in the trash. Composting the waste makes it safe and fertilizes your yard at the same time!

Your Responsibility

It's time to come clean about toxic pollution. Many industries pollute, but so do individuals. People drive cars, create waste, and litter. All of these 70 actions have a negative impact on our environment. We all need to do our part to protect our air, land, and water from toxic waste. What else can you do to help?

- **Write an IVF topic sentence for Ocean Pollution.**

____

____

____

Prepare to Write

Part A. Study the Prompt

Read the prompt and circle the topic. Underline the instructions.

Write a paragraph describing air, land, or water pollution. Make sure to include sensory details in your description.

Part B. Write the Topic Sentence

Use the prompt to write a topic sentence.

_______________ pollution is harmful to the environment.

Part C. Two-Column Notes

Take notes by writing the type of pollution in the left-hand side of the chart. Fill in the descriptive details on the right-hand side.

Topic:	
☆	–
	–
	–
☆	–
	–
	–
☆	–
	–
	–

Prepare to Write (*cont.*)

☆	—
	—
	—
☆	—
	—
	—
☆	—
	—
	—
☆	—
	—
	—

Write It: Topic Sentence Patterns

Write a topic sentence based on the content of "Coming Clean About Toxic Pollution," using each of the following patterns.

1. IVF Topic Sentence

I (Identify the item)	V (select Verb)	F (Finish your thought)
"Batty About Bats!"	explains	facts about bats.

Example topic sentence: "Batty About Bats!" explains facts about bats.

New topic sentence: ______________________________

____

____

2. Number Topic Sentence

Number Word	Topic (What the paragraph will be about)
three	problems led to the Big Dig project
	types of pollution and how they impact the environment

Example topic sentence: Three problems led to the Big Dig project in Boston.

New topic Sentence: ______________________________

____

____

Write It: Topic Sentence Patterns (*cont.*)

3. Turn Prompt Topic Sentence

Prompt	Direction Words	Topic
Write a paragraph that explains how maps are made.	Write an explanatory paragraph	how maps are made
Write a paragraph that describes the negative impacts of pollution.		

Example topic sentence: Maps are made in several layers.

New topic sentence: ______________________________

____

____

Elements of a Descriptive Paragraph

Topic Sentence: ______________________________ is harmful to the environment.

List adjectives and phrases by each sense that can be used to describe your pollution.

Senses	Describing Words
	How does it look?
	How does it sound?
	How does it smell?
	How does it taste?
	How does it feel?

Restate your topic sentence to create a concluding sentence. Think of different words or synonyms you can use. Consider changing the word order or the sentence structure.

____

____

The Expository Writer's Checklist

Trait	Yes	No	Did the writer . . .?
Ideas and Content			clearly state the topic of the composition
			focus each paragraph on the topic
			include examples, evidence, and/or explanations to develop each paragraph
Organization			Paragraph Level:
			tell things in an order that makes sense
			Report Level:
			write an introductory paragraph that states the topic and the plan
			use transition topic sentences to connect paragraphs
			write a concluding paragraph that restates the introductory paragraph
Voice and Audience Awareness			think about the audience and purpose for writing
			write in a clear and engaging way that makes the audience want to read the work
Word Choice			find a unique way to say things
			use words that are lively and specific to the content
Sentence Fluency			write complete sentences
			expand some sentences using the steps of Masterpiece Sentences
			use compound sentence elements and compound sentences
Conventions			capitalize words correctly:
			capitalize the first word of each sentence
			capitalize proper nouns, including people's names
			punctuate correctly:
			end sentences with a period, question mark, or exclamation mark
			use an apostrophe for possessive nouns and contractions
			use commas and/or semicolons correctly
			use grammar correctly:
			use the correct verb tense
			make sure the verb agrees with the subject in number
			use correct spelling

Revise It: Using the Writer's Checklist

Use the Writer's Checklist to edit this paragraph. Check off each item, using Yes or No. Use the editor's marks to revise sentences that need improvement.

Pollution destroys our land the garbage in landfills causes poison in the ground. It is bad for plats and creatures. Pollution also destroys our Water. The air is destroyed by pollution. Toxins are in the air we breathe. Toxins come from household products and cars. They are bad. Pollution is causing problems. Pollution destroys the land, water, and air.

Editor's Marks

∧	add or change text
ℓ	delete text
⬭→	move text
¶	new paragraph
≡	capitalize
/	lowercase
⨀	insert period
⬭	check spelling or spell out word

Word Fluency: Second Read

Read the words fluently.

	Correct	Errors
1st Try		
2nd Try		

smoke	rule	stuck	mask	eve	slush	stick	bikes	tube	let	10
stuck	mask	eve	slush	stick	bikes	tube	let	quite	cute	20
eve	slush	stick	bikes	tube	let	quite	cute	shell	locked	30
stick	bikes	tube	let	quite	cute	shell	locked	shake	shale	40
tube	let	quite	cute	shell	locked	shake	shale	doll	sniffing	50
quite	cute	shell	locked	shake	shale	doll	sniffing	less	quote	60
shell	locked	shake	shale	doll	sniffing	less	quote	rule	smoke	70
shake	shale	doll	sniffing	less	quote	rule	smoke	mask	stuck	80
doll	sniffing	less	quote	rule	smoke	mask	stuck	slush	eve	90
less	quote	rule	smoke	mask	stuck	slush	eve	bikes	tube	100

Four-Square

Write the definition of *spoil*. Then, complete the graphic organizer with synonyms, examples, antonyms, nonexamples, related words, and figurative language.

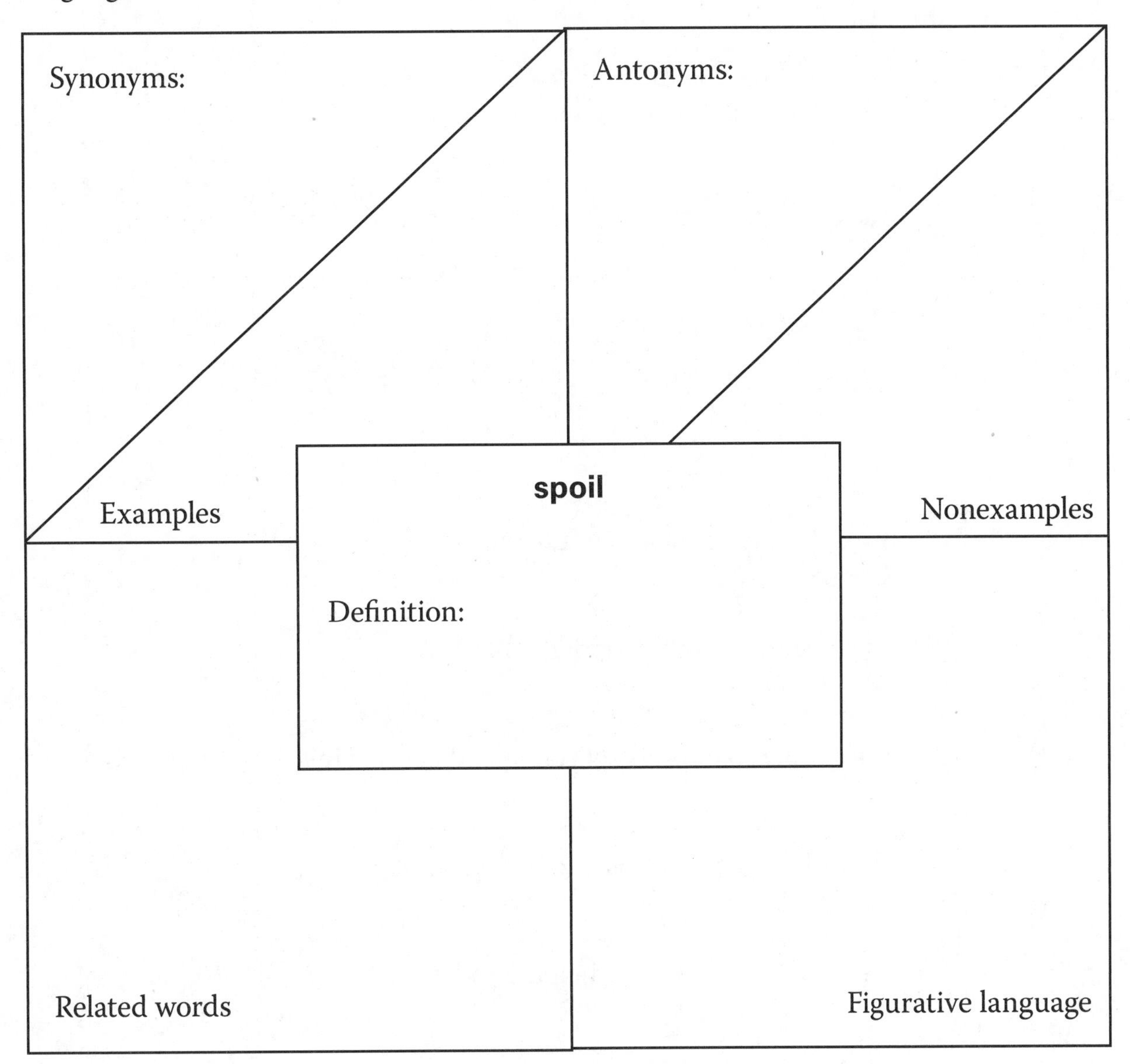

Code It: Subjects and Adjectives

Read each sentence. Write *S* over the noun that is the subject in each sentence and underline the words that modify the subject by telling *how many, what kind,* or *which one.* Write *ADJ* above the underlined words or phrases.

ADJ S

1. The dangerous toxins spilled.

2. The quick rat in the cage sniffed the smelly rope.

3. The lone fox stood still.

4. The box with the ribbon broke.

5. Six tall candles burned in the wind.

6. The harmful pollution clouds the clean air.

7. The simple solution is recycling and conserving.

8. Helpful students put plastic bottles in blue bins.

9. Sixty-five teachers were helping today.

10. Many frogs croaked in the dark pond.

Using Verbs

Part A

Read each sentence. Circle the correct form of the verb to agree with the subject noun or pronoun. Write the word on the line. Read the sentence to check for accuracy.

1. He ________________ the park. (clean or cleans)
2. She ________________ the dead fish. (smell or smells)
3. They ________________ the fish. (harm or harms)
4. The acid rain ________________ plants. (kill or kills)
5. People ________________ cars and trucks. (drive or drives)

List the singular present tense verbs used in these sentences.

____

Part B

Read the sentences. Circle the correct form of the present tense verb for each sentence. Write the word on the line. Read the sentence to check for accuracy.

1. She is ________________ simple changes. (makes or making)
2. Toxic waste ________________ the land, water, and air. (destroys or destroying)
3. They ________________ pesticide on crops. (use or using)
4. The landfill is ________________ toxic substances into the soil. (seeps or seeping)
5. The creature is ________________ the poisonous plants. (eats or eating)

List the present progressive verb forms used in these sentences.

____

Verb Forms: Linking Verbs

Linking verbs connect, or link, the subject to a word in the predicate. They do not describe actions. They give us information about the subject. Forms of the verb ***be*** are often used as linking verbs.

Clas Thunberg **is** the king of speed skating.

The verb ***is*** links the information in the predicate to the subject.

When a noun follows a linking verb, it renames the subject and tells more about it. This noun is called a **predicate nominative**.

When an adjective follows a linking verb, it describes the subject. This adjective is called a **predicate adjective**.

Crossword puzzles are **fun**.

subject — predicate adjective

Diagram It: Linking Verbs

Diagram each sentence.

1. Poisonous chemicals pollute.

2. Toxic waste spoils everything.

3. The dangerous toxins spilled into the lake.

4. The lake is dead.

5. Conservation is important.

Diagram It: Linking Verbs (*cont.*)

6. The device is a catalytic converter.

7. Some factories are polluters.

8. The broken bottles on the beach are a hazard.

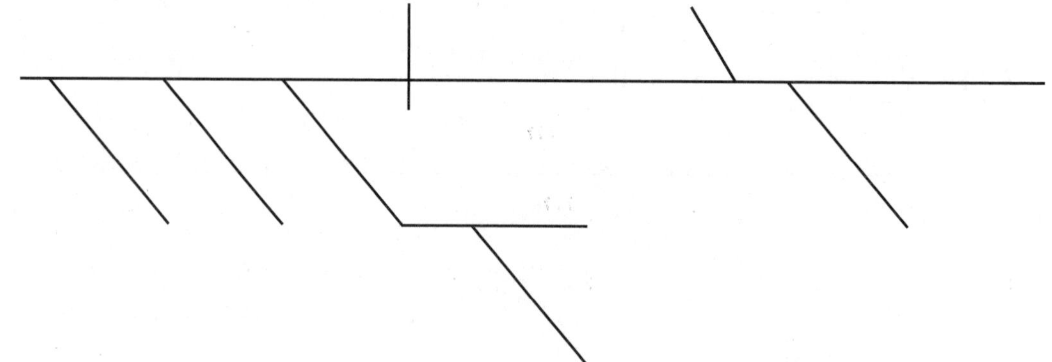

Reading for Fluency

Read the passage with prosody. Chunk the words into phrases and create an image in your head as you read.

Quite a Bike Ride

My name is Jane. My pals and I want to take a long bike ride and be back at the Rams and Cats game by five.

We are in luck. It is June, so we have time for a long ride. We want to ride for ten miles. We will ride to the cove by the docks. Then we will ride up into the hills, by the lake, and up the long slope to the mill. We will ride by the caves. Then, the track will take us back to our base at my home.

We tested our bikes. The bikes were safe, so it was time to ride. We were off. Nell said, "I like to ride fast, but at a safe rate." Abe said, "Kick it up, Nell. I like to ride fast in the mud and slime." Tate said, "This bike is fast. I will pass you, Abe." Off they rode. Nell and I rode at a fast, but safe rate.

We rode by the docks. There were lots of gulls and we smelled the fish. We rode up the lane and into the hills. Tate wove in the ruts like it was a maze. The sun was hot. It was a good time for a ride.

As we rode by the lake, Nell yelled, "There is a snake on the track!" Abe yelled, "Stop as fast as you can, Nell, or you will hit it!" Nell's bike did shake. It slid into a pile of rocks, stones, and sticks. She fell into the slate and shale. The sticks and stones kicked up and hit the bike's spokes. We will not quote what she said as she fell off her bike. I asked her, "Nell, are you OK?" She had cuts on her legs. She hit her nose and it was red. She said, "I am fine." Abe asked, "Can you still ride, Nell?" Nell said, "I am OK, but my bike is in bad shape." Yes, it was a mess.

Tate said, "She cannot ride her bike with the spokes like that. But, she can ride back home on my bike with me. I will not ride fast. I will ride at a safe rate. We must get back or we will miss the game." It was not a fast trip. We rode back to my home. Nell was safe, but she had some nicks on her shins.

What a shame. We wished for a long bike ride. But, five or six miles will have to do. We are safe. And, we made it to the game just in time.

Using New Vocabulary

Fill in the blanks with the appropriate vocabulary words. If you need assistance, use the word bank at the bottom of the page.

A _______________ of toxins _______________ our air. The harmful _______________ found in coal and oil are released into the air when burned. In cities, truck and car exhaust is a major contributor to air _______________.

Today, _______________ machines can measure the quality of the air. These _______________ tell us whether the air is safe to breathe. If the air quality is poor, officials issue an air quality alert. If the air is bad, your eyes and throat might itch.

Humankind needs to take air pollution seriously or we will _______________ the environment on our planet. There are people who are devoted to the environment and keeping the Earth green and the air clean. What can each of us do to _______________ the green movement?

Word Bank

support	pollution	spoil	substances
modern	variety	destroy	devices

Subject-Verb Agreement

Match subjects and predicates to make complete, grammatically correct sentences. Read the complete sentences.

Subjects	Predicates
I	is vast.
The land	is to stop toxins.
Toxic pollution	are in the book.
The task	am Miss Rachel Carson.
The facts	is bad.
The rocks	are in the nest.
Robins	are on the land.
Toxic crops	are green and wet.
The plants in the pond	is too fast for us.
The quick rabbit	are bad for all of us.

Responding to Prompts

Listen to the prompts and possible answers. Fill in the bubble for your answer choice.

Example: State one thing you can do to reduce toxic waste.

To answer this prompt, I need to _____.

- Ⓐ label specific information
- Ⓑ apply information or a procedure
- Ⓒ say or write specific information
- Ⓓ tell or write the meaning or definition

1. Name a toxin that pollutes fish in the sea.

   To answer this prompt, I need to _____.

   - Ⓐ say or write specific information
   - Ⓑ label specific information
   - Ⓒ state a series of names, ideas, or events
   - Ⓓ apply information or a procedure

2. Tell what acid rain does when it falls.

   To answer this prompt, I need to _____.

   - Ⓐ say or write specific information
   - Ⓑ state a series of names, ideas, or events
   - Ⓒ apply information or a procedure
   - Ⓓ label specific information

3. Use the subtitles to find out what the passage is about.

   To answer this prompt, I need to _____.

   - Ⓐ say or write specific information
   - Ⓑ label specific information
   - Ⓒ apply information or a procedure
   - Ⓓ state a series of names, ideas, or events

4. Define what a toxin is.

   To answer this prompt, I need to _____.

   - Ⓐ tell or write the meaning or definition
   - Ⓑ label specific information
   - Ⓒ say or write specific information
   - Ⓓ apply information or a procedure

5. List the different kinds of pollution.

   To answer this prompt, I need to _____.

   - Ⓐ say or write specific information
   - Ⓑ state a series of names, ideas, or events
   - Ⓒ label specific information
   - Ⓓ tell or write the meaning or definition

Adjectives

Listen to the prompts and possible answers. Fill in the bubble for your answer choice.

Example: Choose the adjective in the following sentence:

Some weeds are growing in my garden.

Ⓐ growing
Ⓑ weeds
Ⓒ some
Ⓓ garden

1. Choose the adjective in the following sentence:

   Only eight apples grew on the tree.

   Ⓐ eight
   Ⓑ tree
   Ⓒ apples
   Ⓓ Only

2. Choose the adjective in the following sentence:

   My brother woke up late this morning.

   Ⓐ up
   Ⓑ late
   Ⓒ morning
   Ⓓ this

3. Choose the adjective in the following sentence:

   The front wheel came off the wagon with a crash.

   Ⓐ front
   Ⓑ off
   Ⓒ crash
   Ⓓ wagon

4. Choose the adjective in the following sentence:

   The waves were huge at the beach today.

   Ⓐ waves
   Ⓑ today
   Ⓒ beach
   Ⓓ huge

5. Choose the adjective in the following sentence:

   The worried mother held the children tightly by the hand.

   Ⓐ tightly
   Ⓑ hand
   Ⓒ worried
   Ⓓ children

Inflectional Ending *-ing*

Listen to the prompts and possible answers. Fill in the bubble for your answer choice.

Example: Which verb form correctly completes the following sentence?

We _____ breakfast early today.

Ⓐ eating
Ⓑ am eating
Ⓒ eats
Ⓓ are eating

1. Which verb form correctly completes the following sentence?

   Glenda _____ the test over again.

   Ⓐ is taking
   Ⓑ taking
   Ⓒ are taking
   Ⓓ take

2. Which verb form correctly completes the following sentence?

   I _____ in the back row.

   Ⓐ am sitting
   Ⓑ are sitting
   Ⓒ sitting
   Ⓓ sits

3. Which verb form correctly completes the following sentence?

   The runners _____ after the race.

   Ⓐ rests
   Ⓑ are resting
   Ⓒ resting
   Ⓓ am resting

4. Which verb form correctly completes the following sentence?

   Who _____ down the stairs?

   Ⓐ come
   Ⓑ am coming
   Ⓒ is coming
   Ⓓ coming

5. Which verb form correctly completes the following sentence?

   The leaves _____ yellow.

   Ⓐ is turning
   Ⓑ turns
   Ⓒ turning
   Ⓓ are turning

Let's Focus: "Censorship"

Content Focus
censorship

Type of Text
informational

Author's Purpose

____

Big Ideas
Consider the following Big Idea questions. Write your answer for each question.

Who or what determines what can be seen or heard on TV and radio?

____

____

How has television and radio content changed over time?

____

____

Informational Preview Checklist: "Censorship" on pages 217 and 218.

- ☐ Title: What clue does it provide about the passage?
- ☐ Pictures and Captions: What additional information is added here?
- ☐ Headings: What topics will this text include?
- ☐ Margin Information: What vocabulary is important to understand this text?
- ☐ Maps, Charts, Graphs: Are additional visuals present that will help me understand?

Reading for a Purpose

1. What is the role of the FCC?
2. Which main ideas are supported by the key details provided?
3. How have standards for TV and radio changed over time?
4. In what ways has cable "changed everything"?
5. Why doesn't the FCC fine all questionable content?

Key Passage Vocabulary: "Censorship"

Rate your knowledge of the words. Define the words. Draw a picture to help you remember the definition.

Vocabulary	Knowledge Rating	Definition	Picture
version	0 1 2 3		
specific	0 1 2 3		
appropriate	0 1 2 3		
regulate	0 1 2 3		
interest	0 1 2 3		
permit	0 1 2 3		
coarse	0 1 2 3		
exclude	0 1 2 3		

Are there rules controlling what can be heard or seen on television and radio? When you listen to a song on the radio, does it ever sound different from the **version** on your MP3 player? Have you ever watched a movie on television and noticed that an actor's lips don't match the audio? Why do stations do this? Are there **specific** laws that tell stations what is **appropriate**, or okay?

Radio has been around for more than 100 years, and television has been in the homes of Americans for more than 70 years. Both are "broadcast" over the airwaves, and both are **regulated** by the federal government (unless you have cable or satellite). The FCC, the Federal Communications Commission, was established in the 1930s to protect the **interest** of the people. The government was granted the ability to censor what is heard and seen.

Since the 1950s, the FCC has prohibited, or restricted, the use of inappropriate material. In other words, it has censored what you see on TV and hear on the radio. This has not changed in 60 years. What has changed, however, is the interpretation of what is inappropriate. Is it inappropriate to talk about pregnancy? In the 1950s, the word *pregnant* was prohibited on the sitcom *I Love Lucy.* Is it inappropriate to show a woman's belly button? In the 1960s, *I Dream*

version
a form or variety of something where details are different

specific
relates to a particular thing

appropriate
acceptable for a person, purpose, or occasion

regulate
to control by a rule

interest
anything that helps, or is good for someone or something; benefit

The popular television series I Love Lucy, *circa 1955*

of Jeannie* challenged the standards by showing the main character in a bikini top. However, the actress was not **permitted** to show her belly button. Is it inappropriate to wear a low-cut blouse or show a midriff? In the 1960s, actresses on *Gilligan's Island* pushed the envelope by doing one or the other, but never both at the same time.

The first fine issued by the FCC for violation of the standards was in 1970. Until then, stations set their own standards. **Coarse** language and inappropriate content had been **excluded** from radio and television shows. Belly buttons were not specifically prohibited. It was not against any law to say the word *pregnant*. Television stations placed those limits on themselves.

However, the popularization of cable in the 1980s and the 1990s changed everything. Cable television is able to offer more graphic programming than broadcast television because it cannot be regulated by the FCC. To compete for the viewing audience that watches cable television channels, the broadcast stations have had to relax their standards. The FCC has very rarely issued fines for this. By early 2004, only four violations had been cited. Not wanting to pay fines, television stations appealed the rulings and some of the fines were overturned. Radio stations have consistently challenged the standards. During the same time period, nearly 90 fines were proposed for indecency during a radio broadcast. Talk shows were the biggest offenders. The hosts and their guests discussed topics of an adult nature. The FCC also cited several song lyrics for coarse language.

Today, the FCC still has the power to regulate broadcast networks in radio and television. Mildly inappropriate material can be aired only during the "safe harbor" when children are supposed to be in bed—between 10 p.m. and 6 a.m. However, the definition of "inappropriate" continues to change. What is offensive to one person is not necessarily offensive to another. The FCC does not monitor stations and only responds to complaints. Because they are not monitored, much of the questionable content in programs goes unchallenged and unpunished. Several of the once "forbidden" words have become commonplace during prime-time television, and once inappropriate content appears much more frequently every year. What used to be cause for complaint has now become acceptable.

permit
to allow to be done or occur

coarse
not in good taste; crude

exclude
to keep out; prevent from joining

Multiple-Meaning Map

Determine the meanings of the word *network*. Write the definitions in the boxes.
Use the word in a sentence on the lines below the boxes.

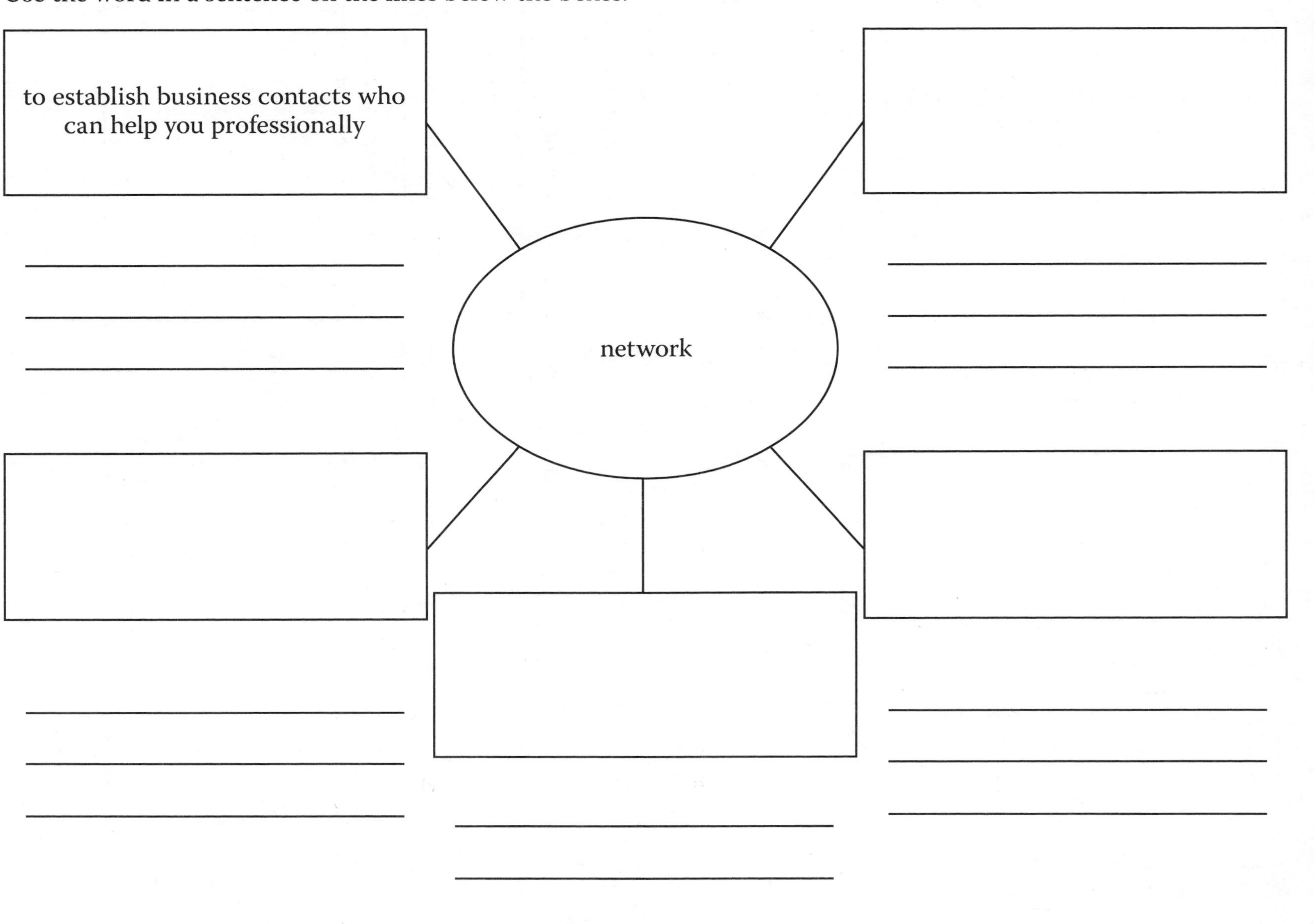

Multiple-Meaning Map

Determine the meanings of the word *average*. Write the definitions in the boxes. Use the word in a sentence on the lines below the boxes.

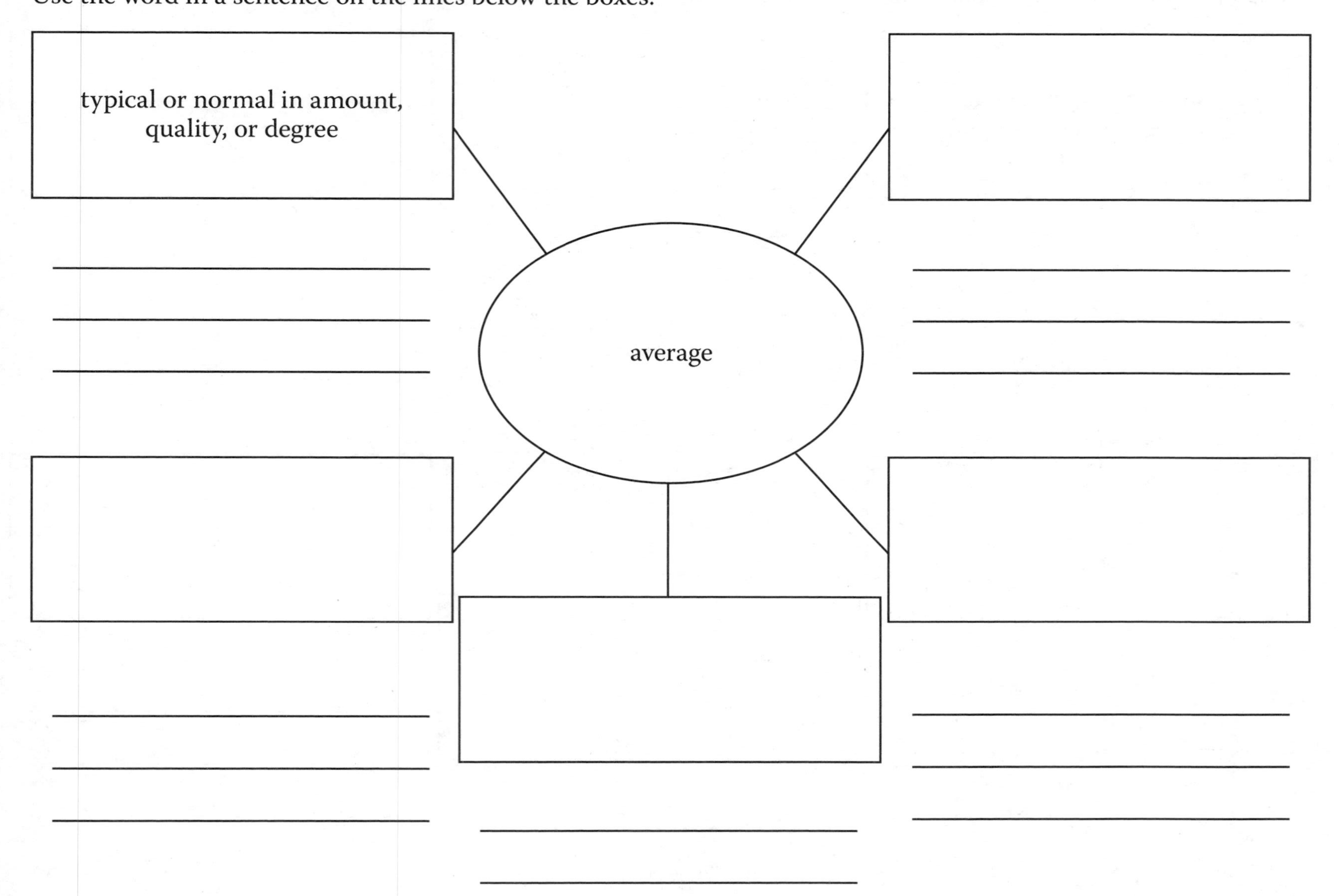

Pronouns

Pronouns are function words that are used in place of nouns. Different groups of pronouns have different functions.

Subject (Nominative) Pronouns

Nominative pronouns take the place of the subject in a sentence.

I, **you**, **he**, **she**, **it**, **we**, **you**, and **they** are nominative pronouns.

Jack sat in a cab.

He sat in a cab.

(**He** replaces **Jack** in the sentence.)

Subject Pronouns		
Person	**Singular**	**Plural**
First Person	I	we
Second Person	you	you
Third Person	he, she, it	they

Find It: Subject Pronouns

In each sentence below, use editing marks to delete the noun that is the subject of each sentence and replace it with a subject pronoun.

Editing Marks	Subject Pronouns
∧ add or change text ℓ delete text	they, he, she, we, it

1. The fox left tracks in the sand.
2. The milkman is quitting at six.
3. The frogs are hopping in the pond.
4. My boss and I discuss how to fix the toxins.
5. Jill is standing on the hill.
6. The boy is cute.
7. Mrs. Smith likes cake.
8. The shake was cold.
9. Glen and I eat meat.
10. The baker, the hiker, and the teacher cleaned for the meeting.

Masterpiece Sentences: Stage 5

Improve your words and be more descriptive by asking more questions.

During the race, the man in the red shirt ran fast on the track.

During the race—*Can you make this more specific?*

During the last lap of the race

man—*Can you choose a more descriptive word?*

the track star

in the red shirt—*Is there a significance to the color red?*

wearing his team's red shirt

ran fast—*Can you choose a better word?* sprinted

on the track—*Can you make the place more meaningful?*

to the finish line

"Painted" Sentence: During the last lap of the race, the track star wearing his team's red shirt sprinted to the finish line.

Before lunch, the little boy grabbed a cookie from the cookie jar.

little—*Can you think of a more related word?* ____________________

boy—*What's a better word for "little boy?"* ____________________

grabbed—*What word would show that he was not supposed to grab a cookie?* ____________________

cookie—*Would it help to say what kind of cookie?* ____________________

____

cookie jar—*What other word can you use instead of "cookie" again?*

____

"Painted" sentence: ____________________

____

____

Identify It: Fact or Opinion Statements

Some statements present facts and some statements present opinions. A factual statement presents information that is either true or false. An opinion statement expresses a belief or feeling. It cannot be proven to be true or false.

Listen as each statement is read aloud. Write *fact* or *opinion* after each statement.

1. The first fine issued by the FCC for a violation of the standards was in 1970. ________________
2. Radio has been around for more than 100 years. ________________
3. The trip was a slap in the face. ________________
4. I was relieved that she wasn't on the computer, but the magazine was almost as bad. ________________
5. We ate dinner as a family, then decided to watch television together. ________________
6. I am unable to shield them from the inappropriate messages bombarding them. ________________
7. They need your voice in Congress to help shield them from the indecency plaguing today's media. ________________
8. The FCC, the Federal Communications Commission, was established in the 1930s to protect the interest of the people. ________________
9. It was not against any law to say the word *pregnant*. ________________
10. Today, the FCC still has the power to regulate broadcast networks in radio and television. ________________

Word Fluency

Read the words fluently.

	Correct	Errors
1st Try		
2nd Try		

cleaning	fuse	slice	wished	clasped	bleaching	chives	cluck	flee	chokes	10
slice	wished	clasped	bleaching	chives	cluck	flee	chokes	plate	steam	20
clasped	bleaching	chives	cluck	flee	chokes	plate	steam	sheep	peeking	30
chives	cluck	flee	chokes	plate	steam	sheep	peeking	chest	stone	40
flee	chokes	plate	steam	sheep	peeking	chest	stone	flute	shocked	50
plate	steam	sheep	peeking	chest	stone	flute	shocked	skates	speed	60
sheep	peeking	chest	stone	flute	shocked	skates	speed	fuse	cleaning	70
chest	stone	flute	shocked	skates	speed	fuse	cleaning	wished	slice	80
flute	shocked	skates	speed	fuse	cleaning	wished	slice	bleaching	clasped	90
skates	speed	fuse	cleaning	wished	slice	bleaching	clasped	cluck	chives	100

Tense Timeline

Sort the underlined verbs in each sentence as present or past tense. Then, circle the present tense verbs in the chart that signal action that is happening right now.

1. Bob asked for a bigger TV.
2. Jack is jazzing up his act.
3. Stan gives the fan to Mick.
4. The crash dented Ted's van.
5. In spring, the robins nest by the house.
6. She calls them to class.
7. The twins edited the text for him.
8. Mr. West is asking the class to finish fast.
9. Cal rested after lunch.
10. They are ending their project.
11. The wax melted in the hot sun.
12. I am investing some cash.
13. We inspected the jet.
14. She passed the jam to me.
15. Today, they take the test.

Tense Timeline	
Past (has already happened)	Present (is happening)

Identify It: Singular and Plural Subjects and Verbs

Read the following sentences, underlining the subjects and circling the verbs. Identify each subject and predicate as singular or plural.

Examples: Some users leave messes in the computer lab. plural

A user leaves a mess in the computer lab. singular

My sister writes a blog about cooking. singular

My sisters write blogs about cooking. plural

1. Wise writers use the spell checker. ________________
2. My aunt edits films on her computer. ________________
3. Workers use computers on so many jobs. ________________
4. In college, some students take exams online. ________________
5. My grandfather invests online. ________________
6. Friends send instant messages back and forth. ________________
7. Those marks make a sideways smiley face. ________________
8. My brother has a good rule. ________________
9. Homework comes first! ________________
10. After that, my brother surfs the Web. ________________

Critical Understandings

Review conceptual understanding prompts on the Critical Understanding chart on page 175 or the poster. Read the prompts to establish a purpose for reading. Then, read the passage and respond to the prompts.

Web Wins

In 2003, a survey showed that young people spend about 16.7 hours online compared with 13.6 hours per week watching TV. In 2006, a survey of teens showed that they spent at least three hours per day on the Web. The 2012 Harris Poll reported that, on average, teens spend 3.6 hours per day online, 2.9 hours watching television, and 1.6 hours each playing video games and listening to an MP3 player.

1. Use the chart to **show** how teens' Internet time compares with their TV time.

Teens' Media	2003	2012
Online		
TV		

Critical Understandings (*cont.*)

2. **Describe** teens' Internet usage over time.

____

____

____

____

____

____

3. **Explain** the results of the 2012 Harris Poll.

____

____

____

4. Choose your favorite form of media from the 2012 survey, and **describe** why it is your favorite.

____

____

____

5. **Summarize** "Web Wins" using an IVF topic sentence.

____

____

____

Phrase Fluency

Read each phrase fluently.

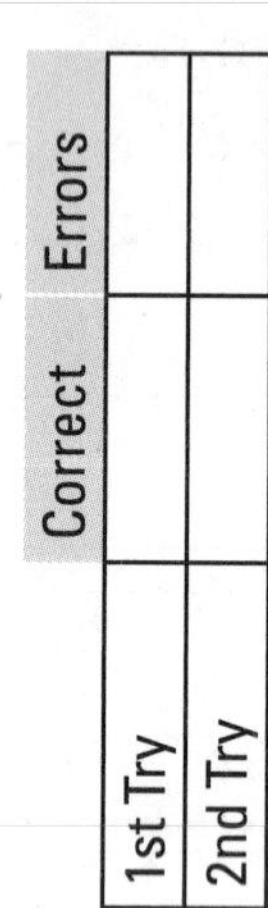

we need	2	the cat's meal	79
he is keeping	5	the man's hat	82
I filled	7	is speeding	84
there are five	10	eating the chips	87
just in time	13	the six sheep	90
some of my pals	17	read his face	93
this week's check	20	about how many	96
my mom said	23	with his meal	99
fly the neat kite	27	my teen pal	102
on the beach	30	is sleeping	104
make a mess	33	was checking	106
my big feet	36	by the week	109
so he tells	39	made it neat	112
no one said	42	my clean cheek	115
Chet's speech	44	each week	117
the hen and chicks	48	he chose	119
were cleaning	50	take a peak	122
up the hill	53	the ripe peach	125
your mom	55	have made the team	129
the long leech	58	was feeding the snakes	133
the team's speech	61	the seeds in the sacks	138
reel in the line	65	flee from the bees	142
cheating on the test	69	Luke's run	144
Chuck's chess game	72	for my meal	147
you do not need	76	are sleeping	149

Phrase Dictation: Subject Pronouns and Possessives

Listen to the phrase and repeat it. Write it in the first column. If the phrase contains a subject pronoun, underline it and write it in the proper column. If the phrase contains a possessive noun, circle it and write it in the proper column.

Phrase	Subject Pronoun	Possessive Noun
1.		
2.		
3.		
4.		
5.		

Use the phrases to complete the following sentences.

1. ______________________ is hanging on the rack.
2. ______________________ my glass with milk.
3. Jack is getting ______________________.
4. If it is hot, ______________________ to turn on the fan.
5. ______________________ the neighbor's cat while she is on vacation.

Phrase It

Read each sentence in phrases. Mark each phrase with a pencil as you read it. Form an image in your mind as you read each phrase. Reread the sentence with prosody.

1. Can I sneak a peek at the chess game?
2. Mom will bleach the rags.
3. She chose red roses for the vase.
4. Jill asked, "Will the seams rip in the cheap jeans?"
5. I like to eat fish and chips.
6. My pal Teal is leading the pack in the bike race.
7. Pete's snack is a ripe peach.
8. Can you see the red fish in the waves?
9. We were feeding the seeds to the chicks.
10. Will you race up Pike's Peak?

Critical Understandings

Read the prompts to establish a purpose for reading. Then, read the information in the chart and respond to the prompts.

A Day in the Life

Let's look at a snapshot of how a typical teen might spend a media day, based on a variety of Nielsen sources: video consumption, led by TV viewing, is the centerpiece of teen media consumption.

Media Consumption of a Typical U.S. Teenager as Measured by Nielsen			
TV 3 hours, 20 minutes	**PC** 52 minutes including applications	**Mobile Voice** 6 minutes	**Video on an MP3 Player** 1 in 4 watched
DVR 8 minutes	**Internet** 23 minutes	**Text Messages** 96 sent or received	**Audio-Only MP3 Player** 1 in 2 used
DVD 17 minutes	**Online Video** If they watched, watched for 6 minutes	**Mobile Video** If they watched, watched for 13 minutes	**Newspaper** 1 in 4 read
Console Gaming 25 minutes	**PC Games** 1 in 10 played, today	**Mobile Web** 1 in 3 used	**Movie Theater** went once in the past 5 weeks

Source: The Nielsen Company

1. **Explain** how text features provide clues about "A Day in the Life."

Critical Understandings (*cont.*)

2. **Use** context to **define** the word *centerpiece* in line 3.

3. **Describe** how teen Internet time was reported by Nielsen as compared with Harris.

4. **Explain** the most surprising result of the Nielsen survey.

5. **Summarize** "A Day in the Life" using an IVF topic sentence.

Ask and Answer Questions

Reread "Censorship." After each section, write a question or prompt for your partner to answer using question or direction words that you have learned so far. Try not to use the same word twice. Be prepared to answer your questions orally. Use the Question Words and Critical Understandings charts to help you.

Paragraph 1 — *How?* *Explain*

1. ______________________________

____

Paragraph 2 — *When?* *Describe*

2. ______________________________

____

Paragraph 3 — *Why?* *Show*

3. ______________________________

____

Paragraphs 4 and 5 — *Who?* *Summarize*

4. ______________________________

____

Paragraph 6 — *What?* *Explain*

5. ______________________________

____

Passage Comprehension

Underline the direction word in each prompt. Then, respond to each prompt using a complete sentence. Write the evidence from the text.

1. Describe the role of the FCC.

____

____

____

Text Evidence: _________________________________

____

____

____

____

____

____

____

____

2. Complete the chart to show which main ideas are supported by the key details provided. Choose from TV, Cable, and Radio.

regulated by FCC	regulated by FCC	not regulated by FCC
more than 100 years old	more than 70 years old	became popular in 1980s
cited with many fines	self-regulated for many years	put pressure on broadcast stations

Passage Comprehension (*cont.*)

3. Using a timeline, show how standards for TV and radio have changed.

1950–1960	1970–2004	Present Day
can't say ____________ ____________	can't show ____________ ____________	mildly inappropriate material can be shown ____________ ____________
	can wear ____________ ____________ ____________	

4. Describe how cable "changed everything."

____

____

____

____

____

____

____

Text Evidence: ____

____

____

____

____

____

____

Passage Comprehension (*cont.*)

5. Explain why the FCC doesn't fine all questionable content.

Text Evidence:

6. Summarize the passage "Censorship" using a single, IVF topic sentence.

7. Choose a time that you used or should have used self-censorship by placing limits on your language or actions. Describe how self-censorship improved or could have improved the situation.

Dear Congressman Whipple:

Please come with me on a journey that I call "Last Saturday." It was a typical Saturday—running kids around, relaxing, and trying to be a positive influence on my children.

The day started when my 2-year-old awoke at 6:00 a.m. Wanting to sleep in for just a little while longer, I allowed her to watch cartoons on the small TV in my room. When I woke up, I began watching the cartoons with her. In just a few minutes, I saw 15 to 20 acts of violence. Did you know that by the time the average American child finishes elementary school, he or she will have seen 8,000 murders on television? When my daughter goes to kindergarten and is sent home from school for fighting, how can I be surprised? She is already very familiar with the violence at age 2.

After breakfast, we left to attend my teenage son's baseball tournament. The trip was a slap in the face. In the 20-mile drive down the interstate, we saw many inappropriate billboards. For 30 minutes, my children were hammered with countless images and messages of indecency. Like an umbrella in a rainstorm, I try to shelter my children from images like these.

After the tournament, we took another route home, but the view was the same. While I made dinner, the two teenagers in my house went to their bedrooms to relax, and my 2-year-old played with her toys. When I checked on each of them, I was shocked. My toddler had made a gun with her fingers. She was running around, pointing at each of her stuffed animals, and making shooting sounds. We do not own a gun and we have never modeled this behavior. Where did she get this from? When I went into my 13-year-old son's room, he was on the computer playing a game. The entire goal of the game was to kill others in a very bloody fashion. With a wide choice of weapons, he earned extra points for making the kill especially grotesque. While I was sitting there, an inappropriate advertisement flashed on the screen. Quick as lightning, he closed it. I am not sure he would have closed it if I had not been in the room. After asking him to turn off the computer, I went into my 16-year-old daughter's room. She was sitting on her bed, flipping through a teen magazine. I was relieved she wasn't on the computer, but the magazine was almost as bad. When she got up to come to dinner, she laid the magazine on the bed. The advertisement she was looking at had a model who couldn't have weighed more than 90 pounds. Will she think this is how her body should look?

We ate dinner as a family, then decided to watch television together. Turning on a station that had "family" in the name, we felt sure we would find a show that would provide a good example for our kids and keep them entertained. Oh boy, were we wrong! We had to turn off the TV within 15 minutes because of indecent messages.

Sir, I am not an overprotective parent. I certainly do not want my children to be locked away like Rapunzel in her tower, but I am unable to shield them from the inappropriate messages bombarding them. When will our government realize that enough is enough? We need to regulate these messages and not allow companies to warp the minds of our youth.

In the interest of our children, I urge you to take a stand. They need your voice in Congress to help shield them from the indecency plaguing today's media.

Respectfully,

Norah Thompson

Norah Thompson

Spelling

Write the words your teacher dictates.

1. ____________
2. ____________
3. ____________
4. ____________
5. ____________
6. ____________
7. ____________
8. ____________
9. ____________
10. ____________
11. ____________
12. ____________

Define It

Determine the category and attributes of each word. Then, write the definition.

Word		Category		Attributes
fine	=		+	

Definition: ______________________________

____

Word		Category		Attributes
indecency	=		+	

Definition: ______________________________

____

Word		Category		Attributes
graphic	=		+	

Definition: ______________________________

____

Word		Category		Attributes
	=		+	

Definition: ______________________________

____

Attributes for Comparison

Read the words and determine the attributes of each word. Compare the words using the attributes.

Word	Size	Color	Shape	Parts
sun				
TV				
mouse				

1. Compare a TV to the sun.

____

____

2. Compare a TV to a mouse.

____

____

Attributes for Comparison (*cont.*)

Function/Purpose	Touch/Texture	Taste	Sound	Smell

3. Compare a mouse to the sun.

____

____

Masterpiece Sentences: Stages 1–5

Use the picture to answer the questions and write a descriptive sentence.

Who or what?	What did she do?
girl	covered
Which one?	**What did she do it to?**
with an upset look on her face	her mouth
What kind?	**When?**
talkative	after she spoke
	Where?
	in class
	How?
	quickly

Write your sentence:

____

____

____

Paint your words:

____

____

____

Author's Craft

Identify the elements used in persuasive writing. Determine the purpose for the elements and provide an example from the letter to the congressman.

1. Point of view:

   a. Definition: ______________________________

   ____

   ____

   b. Importance: ______________________________

   ____

2. Exaggeration:

   a. Purpose: ______________________________

   ____

   b. Examples: ______________________________

   ____

3. Figurative Language:

   a. Purpose: ______________________________

   ____

   b. Examples: ______________________________

   ____

   ____

4. Value statements:

   a. Purpose: ______________________________

   ____

   b. Examples: ______________________________

   ____

Close Reading: Guided Highlighting

Read the text and complete the tasks.

Censorship

Headings
Forbidden Content Becomes Commonplace
FCC: Protector of the People
FCC Issues Fines

Are there rules controlling what can be heard or seen on television and radio? When you listen to a song on the radio, does it ever sound different from the **version** on your MP3 player? Have you ever watched a movie on television and noticed that an actor's lips don't match the audio? 5 Why do stations do this? Are there **specific** laws that tell stations what is **appropriate**, or okay?

Radio has been around for more than 100 years, and television has been in the homes of Americans for more than 70 years. Both are "broadcast" over the airwaves, and both are **regulated** by the federal government (unless you 10 have cable or satellite). The FCC, the Federal Communications Commission, was established in the 1930s to protect the **interest** of the people. The government was granted the ability to censor what is heard and seen.

Since the 1950s, the FCC has prohibited, or restricted, the use of inappropriate material. In other words, it has censored what you see on 15 TV and hear on the radio. This has not changed in 60 years. What has changed, however, is the interpretation of what is inappropriate. Is it inappropriate to talk about pregnancy? In the 1950s, the word *pregnant* was prohibited on the sitcom *I Love Lucy*. Is it inappropriate to show a woman's belly button? In the 1960s, *I Dream of Jeannie* challenged the 20 standards by showing the main character in a bikini top. However, the actress was not **permitted** to show her belly button. Is it inappropriate to wear a low-cut blouse or show a midriff? In the 1960s, actresses on *Gilligan's Island* pushed the envelope by doing one or the other, but never both at the same time.

Close Reading: Guided Highlighting (*cont.*)

25 The first fine issued by the FCC for violation of the standards was in 1970. Until then, stations set their own standards. **Coarse** language and inappropriate content had been **excluded** from radio and television shows. Belly buttons were not specifically prohibited. It was not against any law to say the word *pregnant*. Television stations placed those limits 30 on themselves.

However, the popularization of cable in the 1980s and the 1990s changed everything. Cable television is able to offer more graphic programming than broadcast television because it cannot be regulated by the FCC. To compete for the viewing audience that watches cable television channels, 35 the broadcast stations have had to relax their standards. The FCC has very rarely issued fines for this. By early 2004, only four violations had been cited. Not wanting to pay fines, television stations appealed the rulings and some of the fines were overturned. Radio stations have consistently challenged the standards. During the same time period, nearly 90 fines 40 were proposed for indecency during a radio broadcast. Talk shows were the biggest offenders. The hosts and their guests discussed topics of an adult nature. The FCC also cited several song lyrics for coarse language.

Today, the FCC still has the power to regulate broadcast networks in radio and television. Mildly inappropriate material can be aired only during the 45 "safe harbor" when children are supposed to be in bed—between 10 p.m. and 6 a.m. However, the definition of "inappropriate" continues to change. What is offensive to one person is not necessarily offensive to another. The FCC does not monitor stations and only responds to complaints. Because they are not monitored, much of the questionable content in programs 50 goes unchallenged and unpunished. Several of the once "forbidden" words have become commonplace during prime-time television, and once inappropriate content appears much more frequently every year. What used to be cause for complaint has now become acceptable.

Prepare to Write

Part A. Study the Prompt

Read the prompt and identify the topic and direction words.

What do you think the role of the government should be in monitoring or censoring television and radio broadcasts? Write a paragraph expressing your opinion.

Direction words: ______________________________

Topic: ______________________________

____

Part B. Write the Topic Sentence

Use the prompt to write an Occasion/Position topic sentence.

____

____

____

Part C. Express Your Opinion

1. Make yourself credible: ______________________________

____

2. Emphasis through exaggeration: ______________________________

____

3. Imagery through verbs: ______________________________

____

4. Use of figurative language: ______________________________

____

____

Part D. Write the Concluding Sentence: ______________________________

____

____

Two-Column Notes

Take notes by writing the supporting details in the left-hand side of the chart. Fill in the elaborations on the right-hand side.

Topic:	
☆	–
	–
	–
☆	–
	–
	–
☆	–
	–
	–

Two-Column Notes (*cont.*)

☆	—
	—
	—

Write It: Occasion/Position Topic Sentence

Occasion/Position statements have two parts. The *occasion* gives the reason for writing. The *position* tells what needs to be proved or explained. Occasion/Position statements have special starter words. Read the examples and write a position statement for the last three occasions.

Starter Words			
After	Before	Since	When
Although	Due	Unless	Whenever
As	Even though	Until	While
Because	If		

Examples	
Occasion	*Position*
Even though the stars in space move constantly,	it is impossible to see those changes from Earth.
When the hero was locked in a maze,	he found a clever way to get out.
If your family wants great pizza,	go to Paul's Pizza Parlor.
Since we had a really hot summer,	I believe in global warming.
Although the sound of thunder can seem scary,	lightning is really terrifying.
If you want to get a good grade on a test,	
Although many schools have a dress code,	
Before I start a project,	

Read the words fluently.

	Correct	Errors
1st Try		
2nd Try		

cleaning	fuse	slice	wished	clasped	bleaching	chives	cluck	flee	chokes	10
slice	wished	clasped	bleaching	chives	cluck	flee	chokes	plate	steam	20
clasped	bleaching	chives	cluck	flee	chokes	plate	steam	sheep	peeking	30
chives	cluck	flee	chokes	plate	steam	sheep	peeking	chest	stone	40
flee	chokes	plate	steam	sheep	peeking	chest	stone	flute	shocked	50
plate	steam	sheep	peeking	chest	stone	flute	shocked	skates	speed	60
sheep	peeking	chest	stone	flute	shocked	skates	speed	fuse	cleaning	70
chest	stone	flute	shocked	skates	speed	fuse	cleaning	wished	slice	80
flute	shocked	skates	speed	fuse	cleaning	wished	slice	bleaching	clasped	90
skates	speed	fuse	cleaning	wished	slice	bleaching	clasped	cluck	chives	100

Four-Square

Write the definition of *rule*. complete the graphic organizer with synonyms, examples, antonyms, nonexamples, related words, and figurative language.

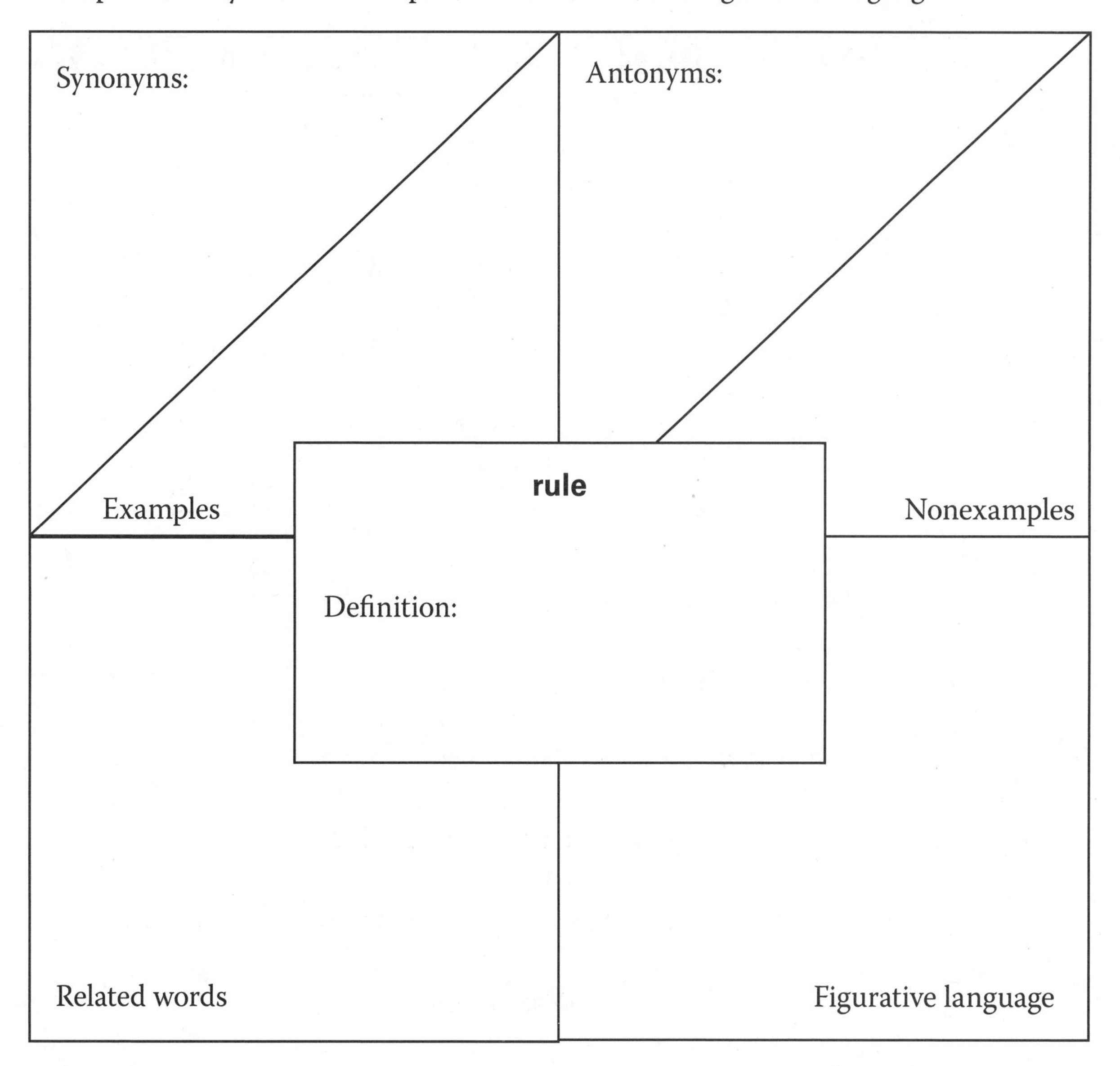

Choose It: Subject Pronouns

Read the following paragraph. Fill in each blank with the correct subject pronoun.

Subject Pronouns						
I	you	she	he	it	we	they

Mrs. Thompson wrote a letter to the congressman. _______________ asked him to speak out for censorship to protect her children. _______________ were driving on the interstate when _______________ saw inappropriate billboards. While _______________ fixed dinner _______________ relaxed and played. Mrs. Thompson was upset to see her toddler shooting an imaginary gun. _______________ was pointed at her stuffed animals. Her older son was playing a computer game. _______________ closed the computer when an inappropriate ad popped up on the screen.

Mrs. Thompson went to check on her daughter. At first, _______________ was relieved to find her daughter reading a magazine. Then, _______________ saw a picture of a very thin model and _______________ upset her. _______________ tried to watch TV as family, but the show was not appropriate. Mrs. Thompson was upset. _______________ begged the congressman to take a stand against indecency.

How do _______________ feel about censorship? The letter made me think. _______________ am not sure how _______________ feel about _______________.

Diagram It: Action Verbs and Linking Verbs

Read the following sentences and diagram each one. Some sentences have action verbs and others have linking verbs.

1. The FCC issued fines in the past.
2. Cable television is popular.
3. Radio stations violated the standards often.
4. The definition of indecency changed over time.
5. Some television shows are funny.

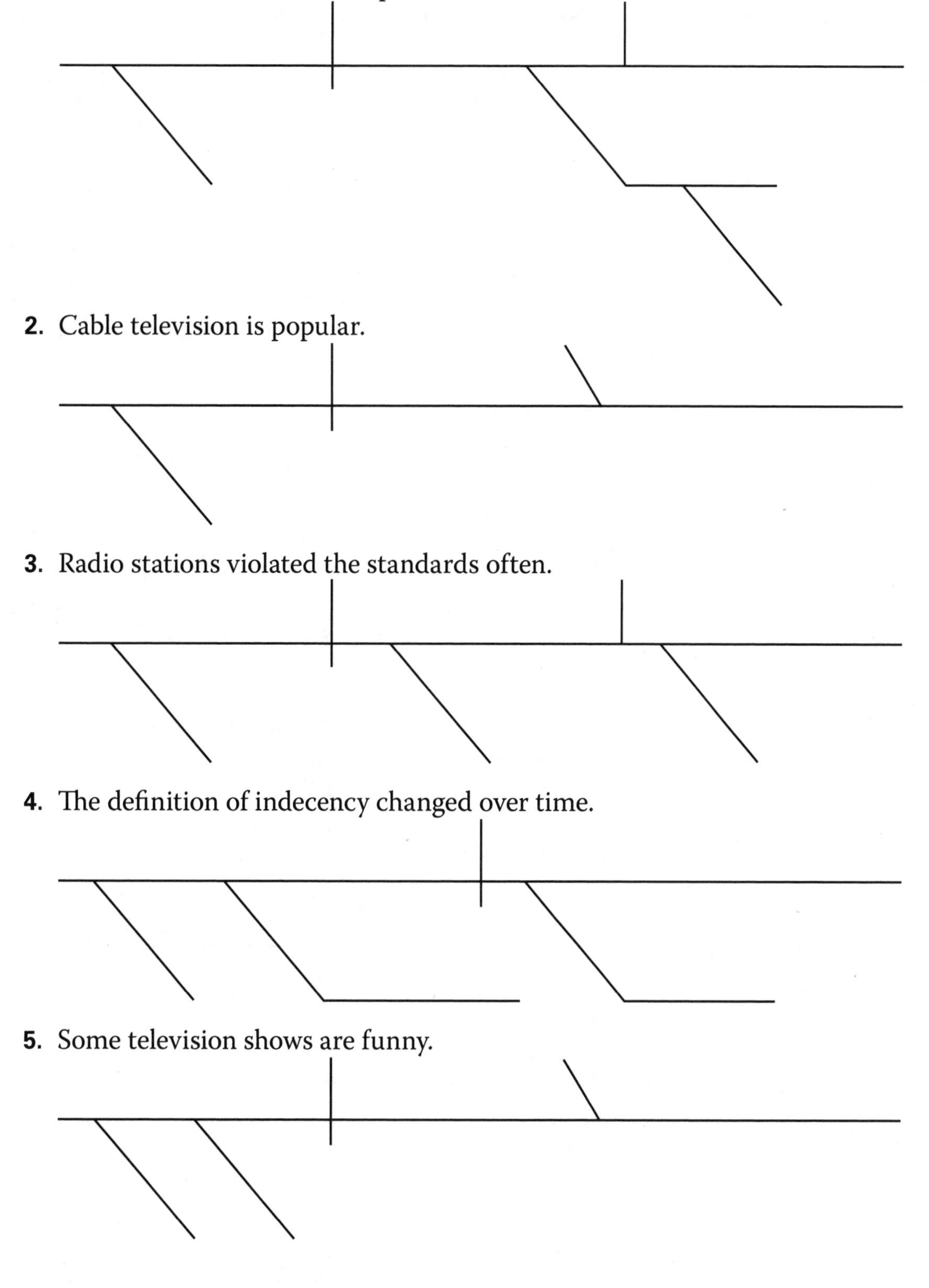

Using New Vocabulary

Fill in the blanks with the appropriate vocabulary words. If you need assistance, use the word bank at the bottom of the page.

Broadcast networks, in an effort to compete with cable, have changed their views of ________________ and inappropriate language. Years ago, ________________ language of any kind was not ________________ on television or radio. Now, only ________________ words are prohibited on broadcast television and radio. However, on cable and satellite networks, crude language and behavior are not always ________________ from the programs. The FCC continues to ________________ what is broadcast over the airwaves. Are the regulations in the public's best ________________? Do you prefer to watch the original ________________ of a show, or the one with the inappropriate content removed?

Word Bank

regulate	coarse	excluded	appropriate
version	interest	permitted	specific

Responding to Prompts

Listen to the prompts and possible answers. Fill in the bubble for your answer choice.

Example: Explain how cable changed the way people watch television.

To answer this prompt, I need to _____.

Ⓐ express my understanding of the changes in cable

Ⓑ tell the most important ideas or concepts about the changes in cable

Ⓒ state detailed information about the changes in cable

Ⓓ demonstrate an understanding of the changes in cable

1. Use a diagram to show the growth in reality television programs.

   To answer this prompt, I need to _____.

   Ⓐ state detailed information about reality television

   Ⓑ tell the most important ideas about reality television

   Ⓒ demonstrate an understanding of reality television

   Ⓓ express an understanding of reality television

2. Describe the relationship between student grades and time spent watching television.

   To answer this prompt, I need to _____.

   Ⓐ express an understanding of the relationship between student grades and time spent watching television

   Ⓑ state detailed information about the relationship between student grades and time spent watching television

   Ⓒ tell the most important ideas or concepts about student grades and time spent watching television

   Ⓓ demonstrate an understanding of the concepts of student grades and watching television

3. Explain the results of the survey.

   To answer this prompt, I need to _____.

   Ⓐ express an understanding of the survey results

   Ⓑ state detailed information about the survey

   Ⓒ tell the most important ideas about the survey

   Ⓓ demonstrate an understanding of the survey

4. Summarize the author's message in her letter to the congressman.

   To answer this prompt, I need to _____.

   Ⓐ demonstrate an understanding of the information in the letter

   Ⓑ express an understanding of the ideas or concepts in the letter

   Ⓒ state details from the letter

   Ⓓ tell the most important ideas or concepts in the letter

Author's Point of View

Listen to the paragraphs, questions, and possible answers. Fill in the bubble for your answer choice.

Example: I am angry. When I walk out of my house, I see that the cushions of my patio furniture have been shredded. I find a dead bird on the lawn. My dog whines and scratches at the door all night. I do not have cats, but my neighbors do. They allow their cats to roam the streets at night while I keep my dog inside, where he belongs.

What is the author's point of view?

Ⓐ Cats are better than dogs.
Ⓑ Cats should not be allowed outside without a leash.
Ⓒ Cats should be kept indoors at night.
Ⓓ Cats are stinky animals.

1. People are becoming television zombies. They come home from work and instead of catching up with their family members, they sit in front of the TV for hours. Children's minds are becoming warped from the violent shows they watch. And adults' minds are twisted by the bizarre reality shows. If those people on TV are supposed to portray reality, I want no part of it!

What is the author's point of view?

Ⓐ Reality shows are a good learning tool.
Ⓑ People watch too much television.
Ⓒ Children should be allowed to watch more TV.
Ⓓ The author is tired of reality.

2. Have you seen those new billboards along the freeway that are like videos? All the people in the cars stare at them—even the drivers. I saw one car almost hit another one because the driver was looking at the billboard. Those billboards are a hazard.

What is the author's point of view?

Ⓐ Highway billboards are distracting.
Ⓑ There should be more billboards with videos.
Ⓒ Drivers should obey the law.
Ⓓ Driving is dangerous.

3. Today my friend bumped a kid in the hall. The kid made his hands into guns and screamed, "You're dead." He could have been hurt. Video games have gotten so real that people forget they're only games, especially when they play them for six hours a day. Don't they have homework?

What is the author's point of view?

Ⓐ Kids need more homework.
Ⓑ Kids should do their homework before playing video games.
Ⓒ Kids should be suspended if they fight at school.
Ⓓ Violent video games are a serious problem.

Author's Point of View (*cont.*)

4. I am so tired of seeing photos of models who are skin and bones. I'm a bit plump, but at least I'm healthy. I've heard that almost 40 percent of models have an eating disorder. Who thinks that's attractive?

What is the author's point of view?

- Ⓐ Underweight models are attractive.
- Ⓑ Eating disorders are not a serious problem.
- Ⓒ Magazine photos of underweight models should be banned.
- Ⓓ Photos of plump models are more like real life.

5. I'm all for freedom of speech, but I'm more in favor of freedom from certain kinds of speech, especially in our school library. If people want sex and violence, there are plenty of other places to find them. If people want their books to be used for education, they need to meet certain standards.

What is the author's point of view?

- Ⓐ Kids need to know about the real world, which includes sex and violence.
- Ⓑ Books about sex and violence should be banned everywhere.
- Ⓒ Some books should be kept out of a school library.
- Ⓓ Freedom of speech is our right.

Subject Pronouns

Listen to the prompts and possible answers. Fill in the bubble for your answer choice.

Example: Choose the subject pronoun to replace the underlined nouns in the following sentence.

Mark and Linda went for a walk.

Ⓐ He
Ⓑ You
Ⓒ They
Ⓓ We

1. Choose the subject pronoun to replace the underlined noun in the following sentence.

Dad mowed the lawn this morning.

Ⓐ It
Ⓑ She
Ⓒ He
Ⓓ They

2. Choose the subject pronoun to replace the underlined noun in the following sentence.

The book fell off the table.

Ⓐ I
Ⓑ It
Ⓒ They
Ⓓ You

3. Choose the subject pronoun to replace the underlined noun in the following sentence.

The woman ran across the street.

Ⓐ He
Ⓑ She
Ⓒ We
Ⓓ They

4. Choose the subject pronoun to replace the underlined noun in the following sentence.

My class went on a field trip.

Ⓐ She
Ⓑ You
Ⓒ He
Ⓓ We

5. Choose the subject pronoun to replace the underlined noun in the following sentence.

The cats played with the balloon until it popped.

Ⓐ They
Ⓑ He
Ⓒ She
Ⓓ We

Past and Present Tense

Listen to the prompts and possible answers. Fill in the bubble for your answer choice.

Example: Choose the verb that shows the underlined action happened in the past.

The cat is licking its fur.

- Ⓐ licked
- Ⓑ will lick
- Ⓒ lick
- Ⓓ licks

1. Choose the verb phrase that shows the underlined action is happening right now.

   Lana pitched the ball fast.

   - Ⓐ is pitching
   - Ⓑ will pitch
   - Ⓒ am pitch
   - Ⓓ pitching

2. Choose the verb that shows the underlined action happened in the past.

   Grandma is calling me this morning.

   - Ⓐ will call
   - Ⓑ call
   - Ⓒ called
   - Ⓓ calls

3. Choose the verb phrase that shows the underlined action is happening right now.

   I walked home today.

   - Ⓐ am walks
   - Ⓑ am walking
   - Ⓒ will walk
   - Ⓓ was walking

4. Choose the verb phrase that shows the underlined action is happening right now.

   The fire truck rushed by.

   - Ⓐ rushing
   - Ⓑ will rush
   - Ⓒ am rush
   - Ⓓ is rushing

5. Choose the verb that shows the underlined action happened in the past.

   The kids are hopping off the circus ride.

   - Ⓐ will hop
   - Ⓑ hop
   - Ⓒ hopped
   - Ⓓ is hopping

Action Verb vs. Linking Verb

Listen to the sentences, prompts, and possible answers. Fill in the bubble for your answer choice.

Example: Which verb form correctly completes the following sentence?

The music _____ too loud.

Ⓐ am
Ⓑ were
Ⓒ are
Ⓓ is

1. Which verb form correctly completes the following sentence?

   The stoplight _____ from red to green.

   Ⓐ changing
   Ⓑ change
   Ⓒ changer
   Ⓓ changed

2. Which verb form correctly completes the following sentence?

   The cats _____ on my bed.

   Ⓐ is purring
   Ⓑ purr
   Ⓒ purrs
   Ⓓ purring

3. Which verb form correctly completes the following sentence?

   She _____ to the store.

   Ⓐ is walking
   Ⓑ walk
   Ⓒ walking
   Ⓓ is walks

4. Which verb form correctly completes the following sentence?

   Dad _____ the lawn.

   Ⓐ mow
   Ⓑ is mowing
   Ⓒ is mowed
   Ⓓ mowing

5. Which verb form correctly completes the following sentence?

   You _____ the fastest runner today.

   Ⓐ was
   Ⓑ is
   Ⓒ were
   Ⓓ am

Batty About Bats!

Flying and Feeding

connect
join together; unite

Bats can fly. They are the only mammals that can fly. Bats use wings to fly. Skin **connects** the arms, hands, and ankles of the bat. The skin makes wings. Wings are important to bats. They need them to fly
5 and find food.

Flying takes lots of energy, so bats eat a lot. Bats eat half their weight each day! Bats eat a lot of things. Some eat fruits and flowers. Some eat frogs and fish. Some eat bugs. They eat mosquitoes and flies. They
10 eat moths and even termites!

Super Sonar

vision
the act of seeing; sight

sonar
a way of locating objects using sound

Did you think bats were blind? They are not. They can see. Some even have good **vision**. Bats fly at night. How do they find their way in the dark? Bats can "see" with sound. They use **sonar**. Bats can hear where they
15 are. Bats cry out. We can't hear these sounds. Bats find their way by listening to the echoes. Bats use other clues too. They hear bugs buzzing in the air. They know where to find a good meal.

The Marianas flying fox eats fruit.

Hanging Out and Helping

Bats hang out. They hang upside down when they sleep. Some bats live in trees or buildings. Some bats live in caves. Millions of bats can live in one cave. Groups of bats living together are called bat **colonies.**

Bats "go to bat" for the Earth. Bats eat a lot of bugs. They save the plants that bugs like to eat. Without bats, bugs could kill a lot of plants. Farmers could lose their farms. Millions of people would be hungry.

Bats also help plants grow. They scatter seeds. There is a fruit in Asia. It is a crop that brings in millions of dollars. What if there were no bats? This plant could not grow. Farmers would lose cash.

colony
group of animals or people living together

Bats in Trouble

Today, bats are in **danger** from us. We destroy their homes. We **interfere** in their colonies. Some people have plans to help the bats. One plan shuts gates to old mines. This keeps people out, but it lets bats in. Some chemicals kill bats. There is a plan to stop using these chemicals. These plans help everyone.

Scientists teach us about bats. Others help bats live. They count bat colonies. They study bats. What can you do for bats?

"There is no point in finding out more about these creatures if we destroy them with **ignorance** and **negligence**," says one expert. "Bats need friends!"

Adapted with permission from "Batty About Bats!"
by Kathiann M. Kowalski

danger
a condition in which something bad or harmful could happen

interfere
to get in the way of; disturb

ignorance
lack of knowledge

negligence
lack of care

A vampire bat goes for a "walk."

Dr. Paul Sereno digs dinosaur bones. He gets a thrill when he digs up the bones of dinosaurs that lived millions of years ago. In 1997, Dr. Sereno led a dig in Niger, Africa. He took 18 scientists with him. The Touareg tribe helped his team look for bones. The Touareg people live in Niger. They know their **desert** land best. They know where to look for bones.

desert
dry place with few plants

The dig was a success. Dr. Sereno's team had a fantastic find. They found a new dinosaur. The Touareg told them a legend about a very big animal. They call it *Jobar.* The Touareg showed them where to look for the bones. The scientists named the dinosaur *Jobaria*. It means "giant." How did they dig up the *Jobaria?* Dr. Sereno followed 10 steps to dig up *Jobaria*.

Step 1: We've Got Some!

The Touareg lead the team to a special place. Bones stick out of desert rock. The Touareg tell the scientists their legend. These bones belong to the giant beast, *Jobar.*

Step 2: Digging In

The dig begins. They use hammers, chisels, and drills. They work for 10 weeks. A huge skeleton **emerges**. It has been buried for 135 million years! Fifteen tons of rock cover it. The team carefully takes the bones from the rock.

emerge
to come out of or appear

The Touareg tribe helped the team.

Step 3: Wrap It Up

They have to make "jackets" to protect the fossils. They cover the bones with paper or foil. They cut burlap strips and dip them in plaster. They wrap each bone with the burlap strips. First, they cover one side. 30 The strip dries into a hard jacket. Then, they cover the other side. They number the jackets. They log each number in the dig's log.

Step 4: Move It Out

The team must take the bones to their lab in Chicago. Twenty tons of bones have to be moved. Some 35 weigh more than 500 pounds. There is no easy way to move them. They use a tripod, **pulleys**, rope, and a chain. They load the bones onto trucks. They drive 1,000 miles to a **port** in Ghana. They put the bones on a ship, which takes them across the Atlantic. Then, the 40 bones are shipped to Chicago.

pulley
small wheel over which a rope moves to help lift or move objects

port
a place on the water where people load and unload ships

Step 5: Unwrap It

The team carefully opens each piece and cleans each bone. They match the numbers on the jackets to 45 the numbers in the dig's log. The bones are put in the right order. Now it's time to rebuild the skeleton.

Step 6: Clean 'Em Up

This step takes two 50 years and hundreds of hours. They use dental tools, tiny jackhammers, and chemicals. The work is careful and **precise**. 55 They have to clean more than 200 bones. These bones came from the adult *Jobaria*. But they have some other bones as well. These 60 are from young *Jobaria*. They clean these bones too.

precise
exact or pays attention to details

Dr. Paul Sereno and his tea[m] at the African dig sit[e]

Dr. Paul Sereno examines the dinosaur bones.

Step 7: And the Missing Pieces?

They have good luck! They have almost all of the adult's bones. What about the ones that are missing? They fill in the missing bones by making them out of 65 foam and clay.

Step 8: Make a Plan

All of the bones are clean. The missing bones are made. At last, they can make a model. From it, they **create** a blueprint. This is the plan to rebuild the skeleton. First, they lay out the tail bones. They place 70 them in order. Next, they study how to put the bones back together. Now, they can see the huge size of the dinosaur.

create
to make

fragile
easily broken or delicate

display
to show or put something in a place where others can see it

Step 9: Copy the Fossils

Jobaria's bones are too heavy and **fragile** to put together. Dr. Sereno's team wants to **display** 75 the dinosaur. What can they do? They copy the skeleton. They make molds. They create copies of the bones.

Step 10: Stack It Up

They attach the casts of the bones to a steel frame. The hard steel frame 80 is covered by the bones.

Finally: Share the Discovery!

They paint the casts to look like the real fossils. They are white with tints of green and red. These colors come from copper and iron in the 85 soil. At last, they pose the dinosaur. It looks so real! You can almost hear that dinosaur roar!

Adapted with permission from "Finding the Pieces... and Putting Them Back Together Again" by Michelle Laliberte

Did You Know?

The ancient Greeks did not know about dinosaurs. But they had a word, *deinos,* that meant "terrible" or "monstrous" and a word, *saur,* that meant "lizard." In the 1800s when scientists began to study fossilized bones of these beasts, they used the Greek words to name them and gave us the word *dinosaur.* Why is "terrible lizard" a good name for these animals?

Pollux
Castor

Gemini: The Twins

On a dark night, turn your eyes up to the sky. The **constellation** Gemini is a sight to see. It has two very bright stars called the Twins. People have known about them for thousands of years. They have been in the sky 5 as long as anyone can remember.

constellation
a group of stars that form a shape

What Are Constellations?

Constellations are fascinating and helpful to many people. They are **patterns** of stars that people see in the sky. These star patterns were invented by people fascinated with the stars. **Ancient poets** of different 10 cultures made up stories about them. Sailors used the stars to navigate across the oceans. Farmers used the stars to tell them when to plant and when to harvest because the same patterns appear in the sky during the same season every year. How long have we been seeing 15 patterns in the night sky? We have done it for at least 6,000 years.

pattern
a picture, image, or design made by repeated items

ancient
very old

poet
a person who writes stories in lines with emotion and rhythm

Why Did the Idea of Constellations Begin?

Constellations are groups of stars with a purpose. Why were star groups made up? There are so many stars! How could we remember them all? We could put 20 them in groups. The groups break the sky into parts. The stars in the sky are divided into 88 constellations. They help us remember which stars are which. How many stars can we see? On a dark night, we see 1,000 to 1,500 stars. Where can we see the Twins? We can 25 see them in the northern hemisphere in November through April. We can see them in the southern hemisphere in December through March.

The Ancient Stories of Gemini

Ancient people invented stories about the Gemini Twins. The Egyptians called them twin plants. The 30 Hindus called them twin gods. Arabs called them twin peacocks. What is the ancient Greek story of Gemini? The Greeks said they were the sons of the Greek god Zeus and the woman Leda. They said that Zeus and Leda had twin sons. Their names were Castor and 35 Pollux. They were **devoted** and loving brothers. They looked alike. But they were not alike. Castor was **mortal** like his mother. He became a horseman. Pollux was immortal like his father. He became a boxer. Both became **expert** soldiers. Castor was killed in battle. 40 Pollux could not bear to be without his twin. Pollux asked his father, Zeus, for help. He asked for Castor to come back to life. Zeus let them be together side by side forever. They are the Twins that shine brightly in the sky. They are the two **brilliant** stars in Gemini.

devoted
loyal; deeply caring

mortal
subject to death; will not live forever

expert
skilled or knowledgeable

brilliant
very bright; giving off lots of light

Look Up

45 When you look up on a dark night, the sky is flooded with star patterns that tell a story.

- Ursa Major (The Great Bear) is identified by the square of the Big Dipper, which forms the bear's body, and a chain of stars, which forms its tail. Ursa Major can be seen in the northern sky throughout the year. 50
- Ursa Minor (Lesser Bear) is identified by the square of the Little Dipper, which forms the bear's body, and a chain of stars, which forms its tail. Ursa Minor can be seen in the northern sky. The North Star is part of this constellation. This bright star has been helpful to nighttime travelers for centuries. 55
- Orion (The Hunter) has some of the brightest stars. He is positioned in the sky to fight off a raging bull. Orion stands with his right arm holding a great club uplifted in the air, ready to strike. Over his left arm hangs a lion's skin that he holds up as a shield in front of him to stop the raging bull. Taurus the Mighty Bull is a constellation that is charging right for Orion. Orion is visible throughout the world. We can see this constellation between December and April. 60 65
- Leo (The Lion) is one of the easiest constellations to find. An easy way to spot Leo is to look for a backward question mark in the sky, which represents the head and front of the body. In the northern hemisphere, Leo can be located in spring, and in the southern hemisphere it can be located in autumn. 70 75
- Centaurus (The Centaur) has the greatest number of visible stars in it. It has 101 stars.
- Hydra (The Water Snake) is the largest constellation. It covers more than 3% of the sky.

Constellations shown above
TOP: Ursa Major, MIDDLE: Orion, BOTTOM: Leo

Jazz began with a "**recipe**" that had many different ingredients. Different groups of people, including Africans and Europeans, were part of the recipe. Different kinds of music, including the blues and ragtime, were also a part of the recipe. All of these ingredients combined to make America's own music, jazz.

recipe
a list of the things needed and directions for making something

Workers sang songs during the long workday. They sang in fields and on ships. They sang while working on the railroads. The work song was an important part of their day. With tools in their hands, they worked to a **steady** beat. The songs made life a little easier. There were many kinds of work songs, and these songs played a part in jazz.

steady
not subject to change; constant

Church music was important to jazz. African Americans made new kinds of church music. They formed their own churches and rewrote the old songs to express their faith. They changed the words, the beat, and the tune. They used the African "call and response" when they sang. This music became an ingredient in the jazz recipe.

simple
having few parts; easy to understand

plantation
a large farm where crops are grown

social
friendly; involving several people

demand
requirement; need

combine
to put together; to join

express
to communicate in words

Music of immigrant Americans added to jazz. The Scotch-Irish had ballads. Ballads tell stories of heroes and their bravery, and these stories are often sad. The song is usually **simple**. In a ballad, the story is 25 often more important than the music. Ballads became another ingredient in the jazz recipe.

In the early days of America, ballroom dance music provided popular entertainment. In the South, dances were held on **plantations**. They were big **social** 30 events. There was a **demand** for musicians to play at the dances. Many slaves learned how to play fiddles and flutes. African Americans invented the banjo and played it too. Black musicians learned the dance songs and changed them. African and European music 35 **combined** to make dance music. This music became another ingredient in the jazz recipe.

During the 1800s, a new kind of music called ragtime was born. It was loud and fun. Musicians pounded on their pianos. They made up songs to 40 **express** their appreciation for music. They played in dance halls. The tunes were lively, and the rhythm was catchy. Everybody loved ragtime. It had a strong, irregular beat that was surprising. Ragtime became another ingredient in the jazz recipe.

45 Sometime in the late 1800s, musicians began to play the blues. Slaves had been freed, but life was still hard. People were sad and frustrated. They expressed their feelings in music. They called it the blues. Today, people still sing the blues when they're sad. The blues 50 became the final ingredient in the recipe.

The jazz recipe came together in New Orleans. By 1890, New Orleans was one of America's most musical cities. It had opera houses and concert halls. It had dance ballrooms and street parades. It had Mardi Gras! 55 Many different people lived there. Africans and Native Americans lived in New Orleans. The French and Spanish also lived there. People from many places and cultures created America's own music, jazz.

Adapted with permission from "Jazz Ingredients" by Heather Mitchell Amey

Coming Clean About Toxic Pollution

Toxic Waste

Toxic waste **spoils** everything. It **destroys** our land, water, air, plants, and animals. A toxic **substance**, even a small amount, can harm plant or animal life. Where does toxic waste come from? It can come from 5 factories that make a wide range of products. It can come from pesticides sprayed on the land. When we throw things away, toxic substances get buried in our landfills. When it rains, toxic pollutants in the ground are washed into rivers, lakes, and oceans. How do these 10 toxins impact our environment?

Air Pollution

Toxins impact the quality of our air. Air supplies the oxygen we need. When toxic substances fill the air, we breathe them into our lungs. When the air is polluted, we breathe in harmful gases and fumes. We 15 breathe in poison! We can't always see the **pollution**. Sometimes, we see it as a dirty mist called smog. Household products like lighter fluid and aerosol sprays contribute to smog. The fumes that come from cars and trucks also make smog. Most **modern** cars 20 have a **device** called a catalytic converter. This device treats the exhaust before the fumes leave the car, removing harmful substances. What can we do to help? Make simple changes in our daily lives. Avoid using lighter fluid. Replace aerosol deodorant and hairspray 25 with solids, gels, or liquids.

spoil
to harm or damage something

destroy
to damage, ruin, or harm beyond repair

substance
what something is made from

pollution
the waste or poisonous substances put into the air, water, or land

modern
having to do with present time

device
a machine or tool that has a special use

Emissions from power plants react with sunlight and moisture to create acid rain.

Land Pollution

Our land is also negatively impacted by toxins. In the 1960s, the average person created approximately 2.7 pounds of garbage each day. By 2007, that number had almost doubled to 4.6 pounds of garbage each day. Where does all of this garbage go every day? Most of it goes into landfills where toxic substances can seep into the soil. Pesticides and fertilizers used by farmers can also soak into the land, causing pollution. Poisons in the ground are absorbed by plants and any creature that eats the plants. What can we do to help? Create less garbage by recycling. Drink water from the faucet instead of in plastic bottles. Look for foods grown without pesticides.

Acid Rain

Acid rain illustrates how pollution spreads and impacts all aspects of the environment. When air pollution combines with water in the air, acid rain is created. Gases that come from vehicles and power plants pollute the air, making acid rain possible. Wherever acid rain falls, it damages the environment. It can kill plants on land as well as creatures in lakes and streams. It is corrosive enough to damage stone structures. It eats away at stone, causing permanent damage to buildings and statues. What can we do to help? We can drive more fuel-efficient cars and reduce our energy consumption.

River Pollution

Pollution threatens all of our water resources. There are many toxins in our homes. These include paint thinner, cleaning supplies, bug spray, and fertilizer.

When toxins are washed down the drain, they get into
55 our sewers and eventually our rivers. If these toxins are buried in landfills, the rain can flush them into rivers. There, they harm the fish and other forms of life. What can we do to help? We can limit our use of water and discard household chemicals safely.

Dead Lakes

60 Our lakes are also damaged by pollution. It disturbs the balance between a **variety** of plants and living creatures. Pollution falls or seeps into the lake. Different types of pollution can make water plants like algae grow rapidly. The algae block the sunlight and
65 use up all the water's oxygen. All living organisms in the lake, including fish, die. The lake is dead. A dead lake cannot **support** life. The animals that relied on the lake for food are also at risk. What can we do to help? We can remember that polluting the land means
70 polluting the water! Stopping the litter that enters our lakes can make a difference.

variety
a number of different kinds or types

support
to have what is needed to maintain or keep something going

Ocean Pollution

In addition to polluting lakes and rivers, many of the toxic substances produced on land end up in our oceans. When waste pours into the sea, it may be
75 eaten by small fish. When bigger fish and sea animals eat those fish, the toxins build up to dangerous levels. Mercury impacted tuna in this way. As creatures poisoned with mercury were eaten by other animals, the mercury levels rose to unsafe levels. Eventually, the
80 mercury levels found in tuna made them unsafe for humans to eat. The effects of pollution on sea life and shore wildlife can be terrible. We cannot think of the ocean as a place to dump our waste. What can we do to help? Recycle and dispose of our trash responsibly. Get
85 rid of pet waste properly so that it doesn't contaminate our water sources. Pick up after your dog. Flush the waste down the toilet or double wrap it and throw it in the trash. Composting the waste makes it safe and fertilizes your yard at the same time!

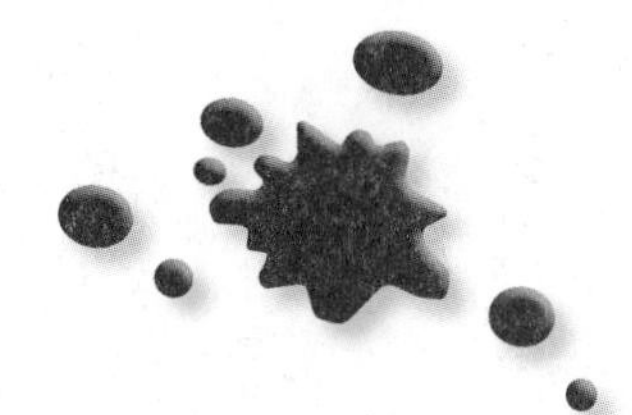

Your Responsibility

90 It's time to come clean about toxic pollution. Many industries pollute, but so do individuals. People drive cars, create waste, and litter. All of these actions have a negative impact on our environment. We all need to do our part to protect our air, land, and water from toxic
95 waste. What else can you do to help?

Are there rules controlling what can be heard or seen on television and radio? When you listen to a song on the radio, does it ever sound different from the **version** on your MP3 player? Have you ever watched a movie on television and noticed that an actor's lips don't match the audio? Why do stations do this? Are there **specific** laws that tell stations what is **appropriate**, or okay?

Radio has been around for more than 100 years, and television has been in the homes of Americans for more than 70 years. Both are "broadcast" over the airwaves, and both are **regulated** by the federal government (unless you have cable or satellite). The FCC, the Federal Communications Commission, was established in the 1930s to protect the **interest** of the people. The government was granted the ability to censor what is heard and seen.

Since the 1950s, the FCC has prohibited, or restricted, the use of inappropriate material. In other words, it has censored what you see on TV and hear on the radio. This has not changed in 60 years. What has changed, however, is the interpretation of what is inappropriate. Is it inappropriate to talk about pregnancy? In the 1950s, the word *pregnant* was prohibited on the sitcom *I Love Lucy*. Is it inappropriate to show a woman's belly button? In the 1960s, *I Dream*

version
a form or variety of something where details are different

specific
relates to a particular thing

appropriate
acceptable for a person, purpose, or occasion

regulate
to control by a rule

interest
anything that helps, or is good for someone or something; benefit

The popular television series I Love Lucy, *circa 1955*

of Jeannie challenged the standards by showing the main character in a bikini top. However, the actress was not **permitted** to show her belly button. Is it inappropriate to wear a low-cut blouse or show a midriff? In the 1960s, actresses on *Gilligan's Island* pushed the envelope by doing one or the other, but never both at the same time.

The first fine issued by the FCC for violation of the standards was in 1970. Until then, stations set their own standards. **Coarse** language and inappropriate content had been **excluded** from radio and television shows. Belly buttons were not specifically prohibited. It was not against any law to say the word *pregnant*. Television stations placed those limits on themselves.

However, the popularization of cable in the 1980s and the 1990s changed everything. Cable television is able to offer more graphic programming than broadcast television because it cannot be regulated by the FCC. To compete for the viewing audience that watches cable television channels, the broadcast stations have had to relax their standards. The FCC has very rarely issued fines for this. By early 2004, only four violations had been cited. Not wanting to pay fines, television stations appealed the rulings and some of the fines were overturned. Radio stations have consistently challenged the standards. During the same time period, nearly 90 fines were proposed for indecency during a radio broadcast. Talk shows were the biggest offenders. The hosts and their guests discussed topics of an adult nature. The FCC also cited several song lyrics for coarse language.

Today, the FCC still has the power to regulate broadcast networks in radio and television. Mildly inappropriate material can be aired only during the "safe harbor" when children are supposed to be in bed—between 10 p.m. and 6 a.m. However, the definition of "inappropriate" continues to change. What is offensive to one person is not necessarily offensive to another. The FCC does not monitor stations and only responds to complaints. Because they are not monitored, much of the questionable content in programs goes unchallenged and unpunished. Several of the once "forbidden" words have become commonplace during prime-time television, and once inappropriate content appears much more frequently every year. What used to be cause for complaint has now become acceptable.

permit
to allow to be done or occur

coarse
not in good taste; crude

exclude
to keep out; prevent from joining

Dear Congressman Whipple:

Please come with me on a journey that I call "Last Saturday." It was a typical Saturday—running kids around, relaxing, and trying to be a positive influence on my children.

The day started when my 2-year-old awoke at 6:00 a.m. Wanting to sleep in for just a little while longer, I allowed her to watch cartoons on the small TV in my room. When I woke up, I began watching the cartoons with her. In just a few minutes, I saw 15 to 20 acts of violence. Did you know that by the time the average American child finishes elementary school, he or she will have seen 8,000 murders on television? When my daughter goes to kindergarten and is sent home from school for fighting, how can I be surprised? She is already very familiar with the violence at age 2.

After breakfast, we left to attend my teenage son's baseball tournament. The trip was a slap in the face. In the 20-mile drive down the interstate, we saw many inappropriate billboards. For 30 minutes, my children were hammered with countless images and messages of indecency. Like an umbrella in a rainstorm, I try to shelter my children from images like these.

After the tournament, we took another route home, but the view was the same. While I made dinner, the two teenagers in my house went to their bedrooms to relax, and my 2-year-old played with her toys. When I checked on each of them, I was shocked. My toddler had made a gun with her fingers. She was running around, pointing at each of her stuffed animals, and making shooting sounds. We do not own a gun and we have never modeled this behavior. Where did she get this from? When I went into my 13-year-old son's room, he was on the computer playing a game. The entire goal of the game was to kill others in a very bloody fashion. With a wide choice of weapons, he earned extra points for making the kill especially grotesque. While I was sitting there, an inappropriate advertisement flashed on the screen. Quick as lightning, he closed it. I am not sure he would have closed it if I had not been in the room. After asking him to turn off the computer, I went into my 16-year-old daughter's room. She was sitting on her bed, flipping through a teen magazine. I was relieved she wasn't on the computer, but the magazine was almost as bad. When she got up to come to dinner, she laid the magazine on the bed. The advertisement she was looking at had a model who couldn't have weighed more than 90 pounds. Will she think this is how her body should look?

We ate dinner as a family, then decided to watch television together. Turning on a station that had "family" in the name, we felt sure we would find a show that would provide a good example for our kids and keep them entertained. Oh boy, were we wrong! We had to turn off the TV within 15 minutes because of indecent messages.

Sir, I am not an overprotective parent. I certainly do not want my children to be locked away like Rapunzel in her tower, but I am unable to shield them from the inappropriate messages bombarding them. When will our government realize that enough is enough? We need to regulate these messages and not allow companies to warp the minds of our youth.

In the interest of our children, I urge you to take a stand. They need your voice in Congress to help shield them from the indecency plaguing today's media.

Respectfully,

Norah Thompson

Norah Thompson

Word Fluency Chart

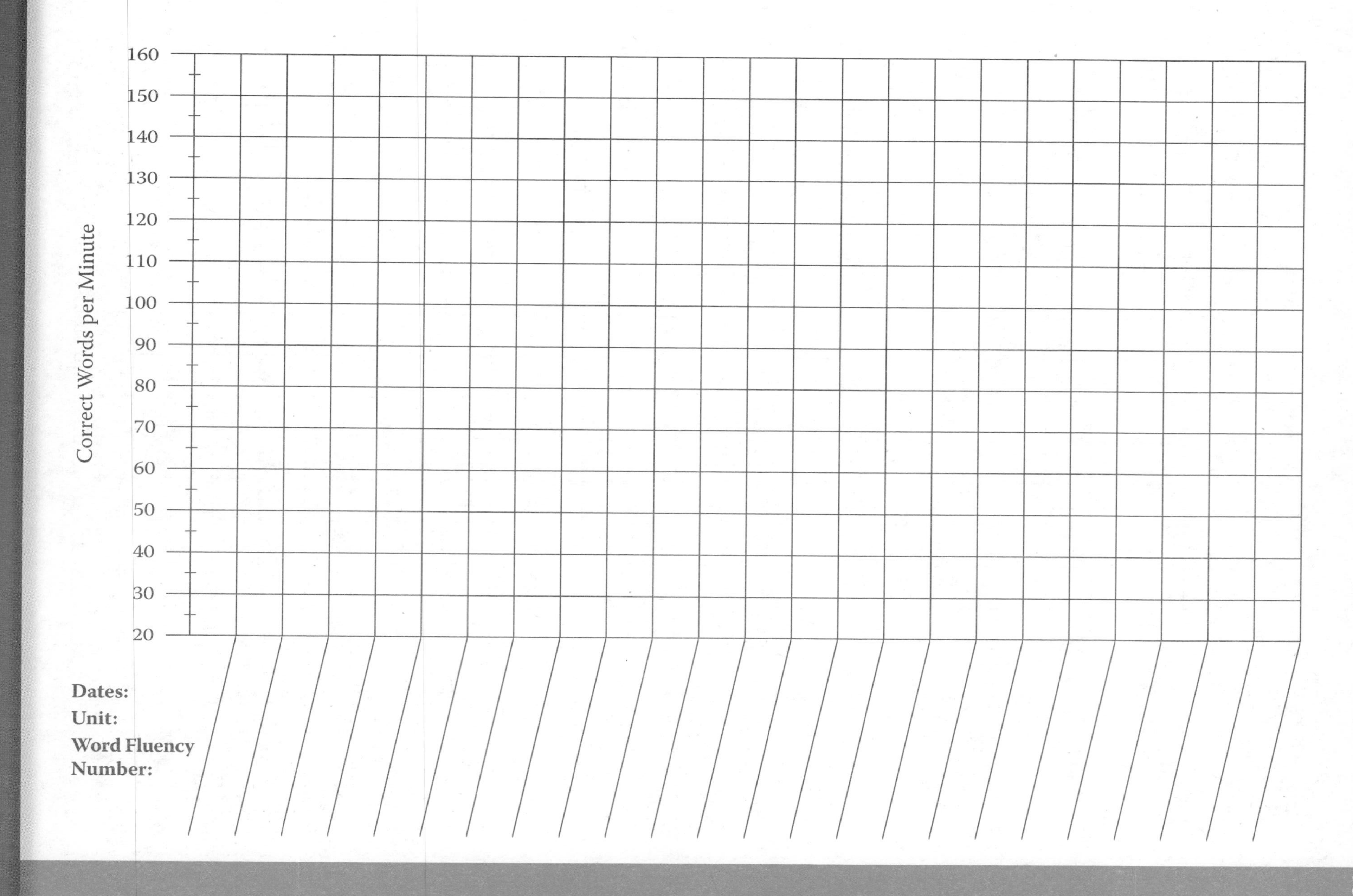
Word Fluency Chart
Correct Words per Minute
160
150
140
130
120
110
100
90
80
70
60
50
40
30
20
Dates:
Unit:
Word Fluency
Number:

Phrase Fluency Chart

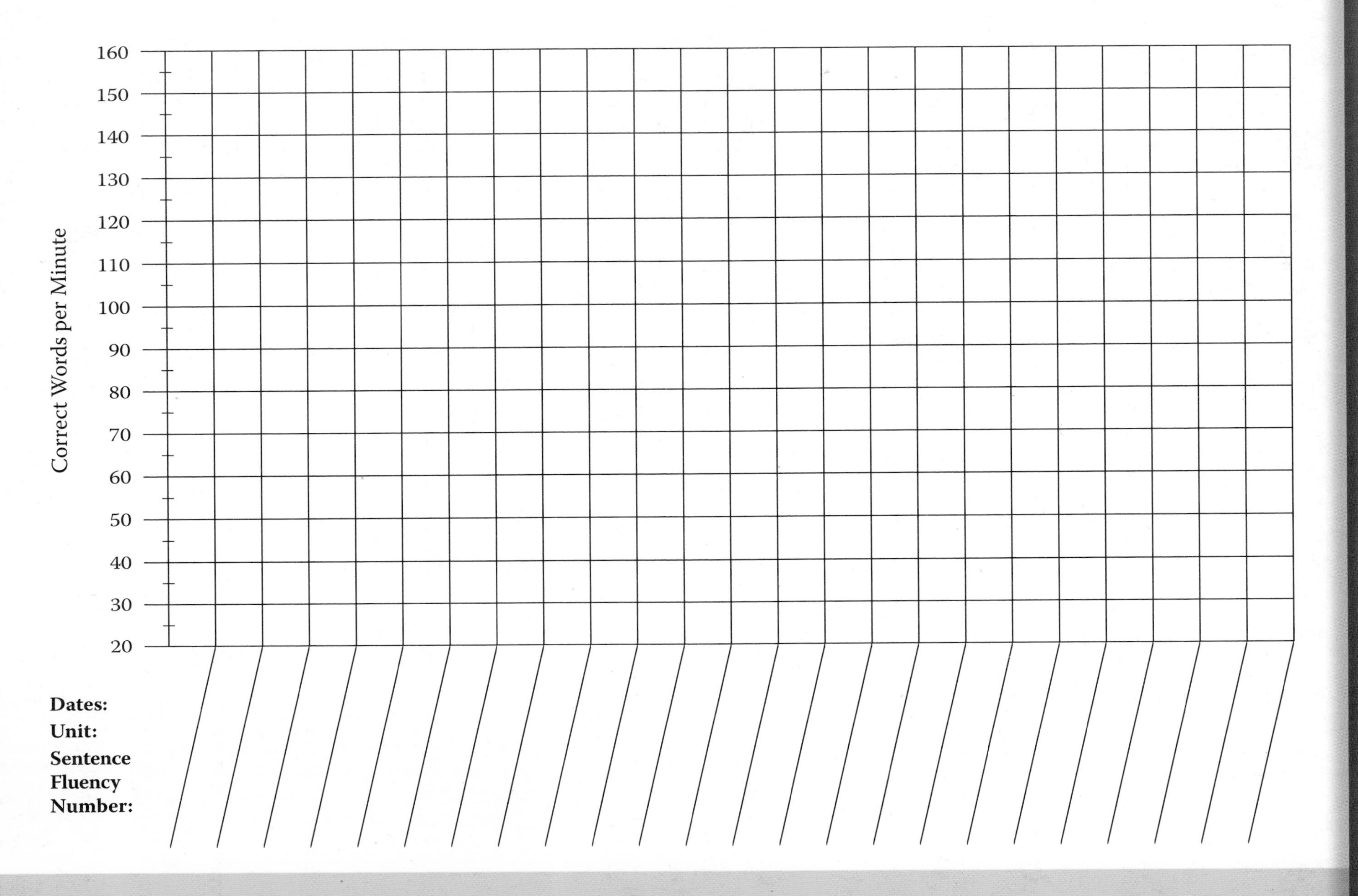

Correct Words per Minute
20
30
40
50
60
70
80
90
100
110
120
130
140
150
160
Dates:
Unit:
Phrase
Fluency
Number:

Key Passage Vocabulary

Vocabulary	Knowledge Rating	Definition	Picture
	0 1 2 3		
	0 1 2 3		
	0 1 2 3		
	0 1 2 3		
	0 1 2 3		
	0 1 2 3		
	0 1 2 3		
	0 1 2 3		

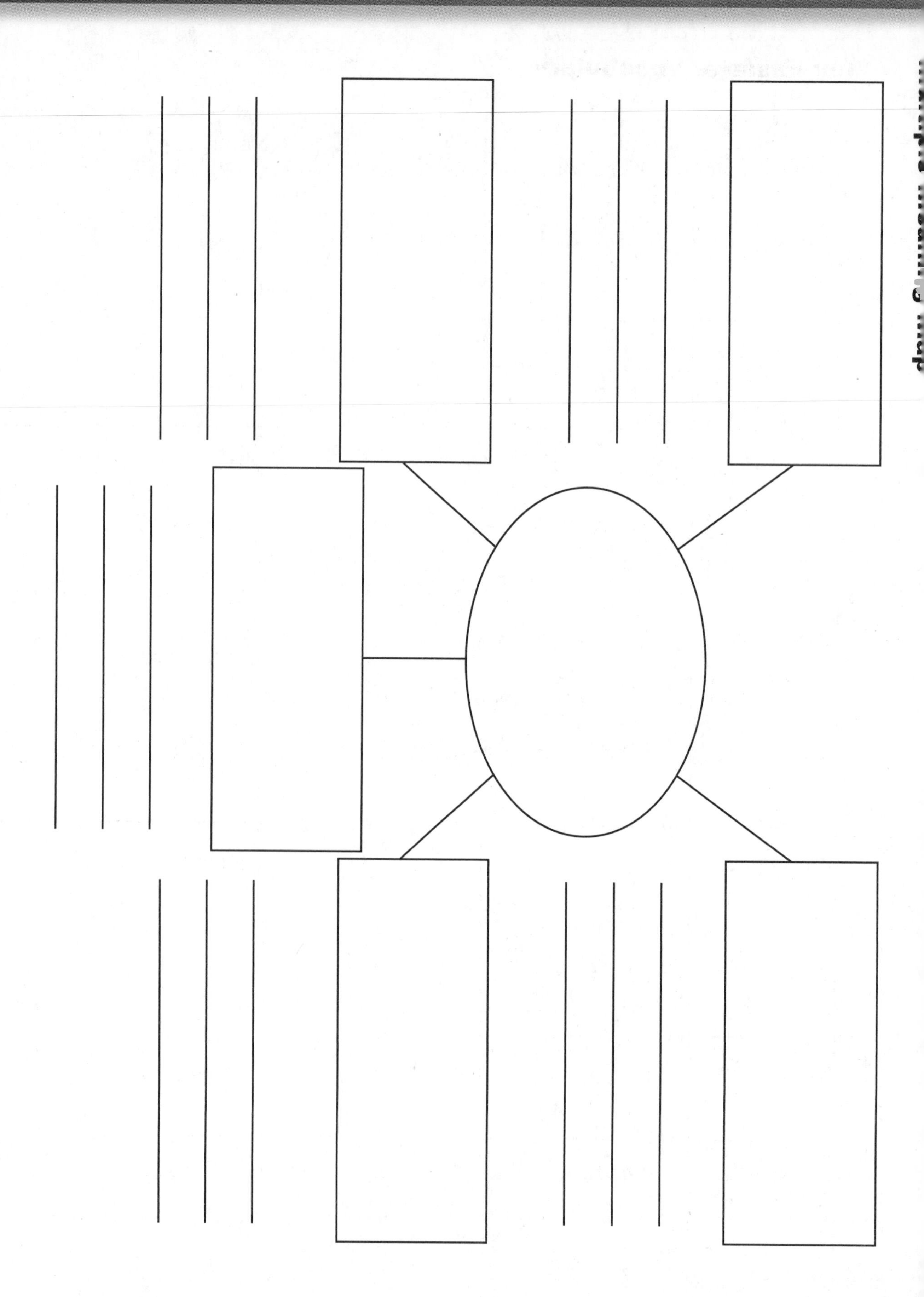

Four-Square

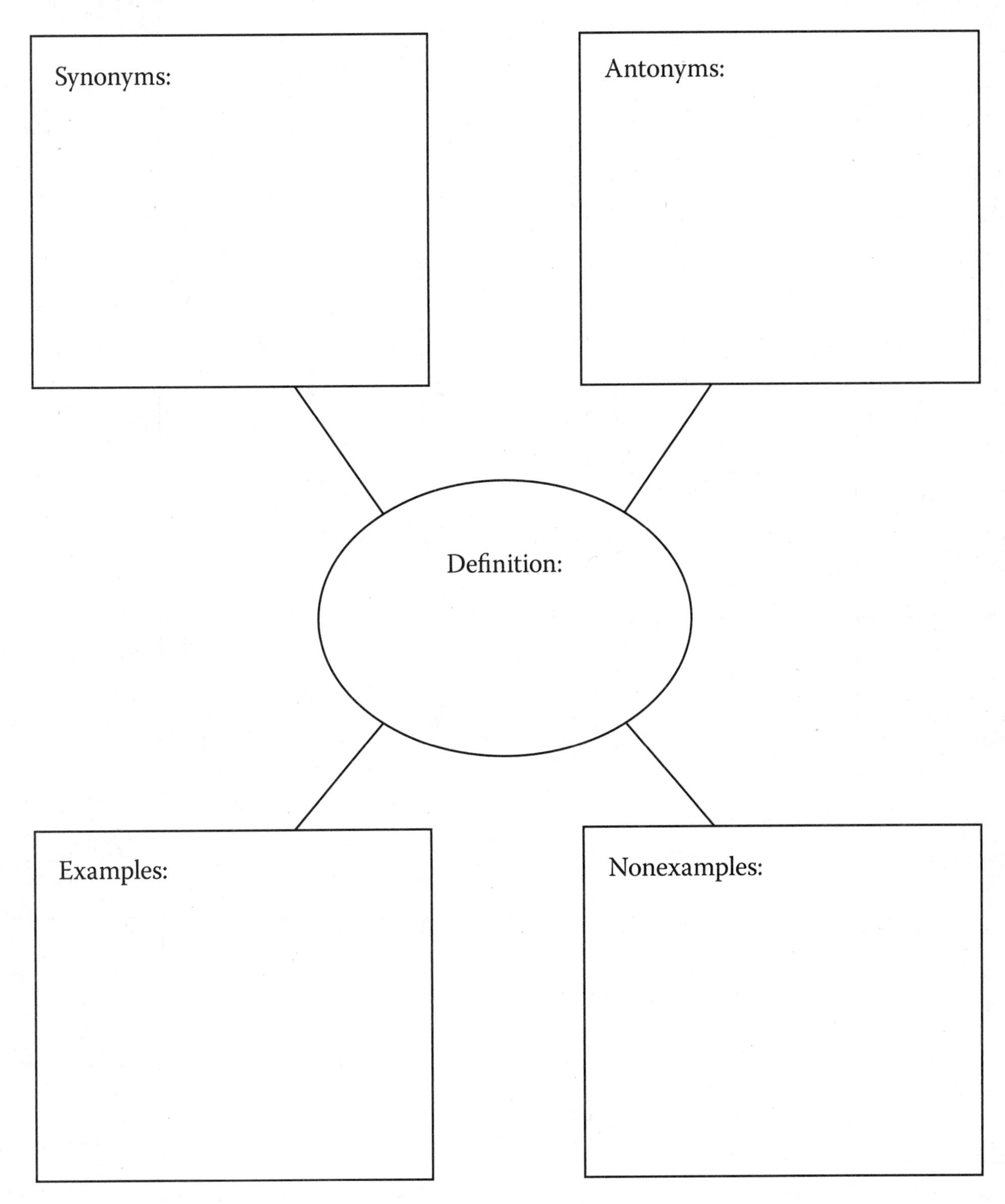

Advanced Four-Square

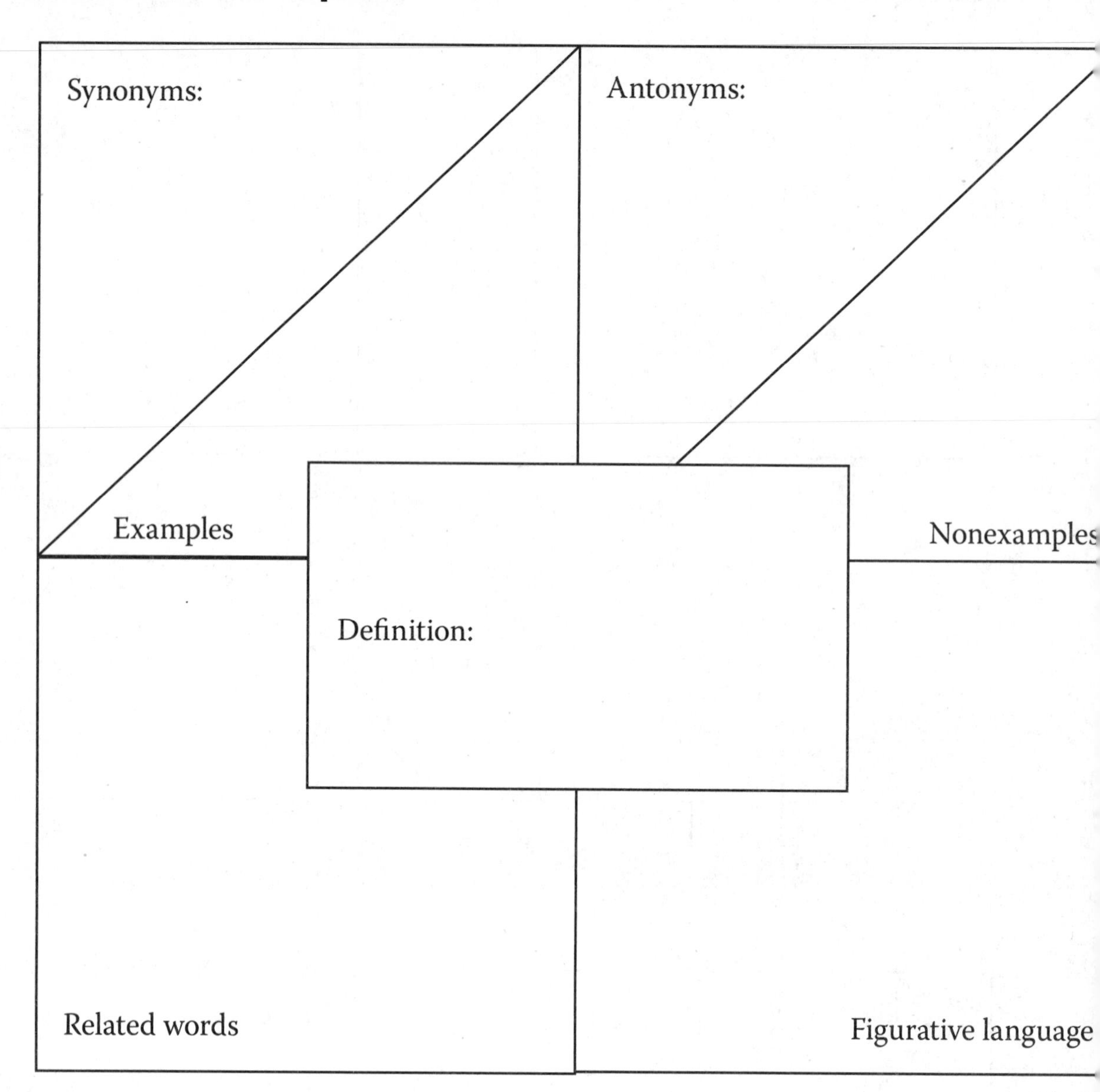

Define It

Word		Category		Attributes
	=		+	

Definition: ______________________________

____

Word		Category		Attributes
	=		+	

Definition: ______________________________

____

Word		Category		Attributes
	=		+	

Definition: ______________________________

____

Word		Category		Attributes
	=		+	

Definition: ______________________________

____

Blueprint for Writing

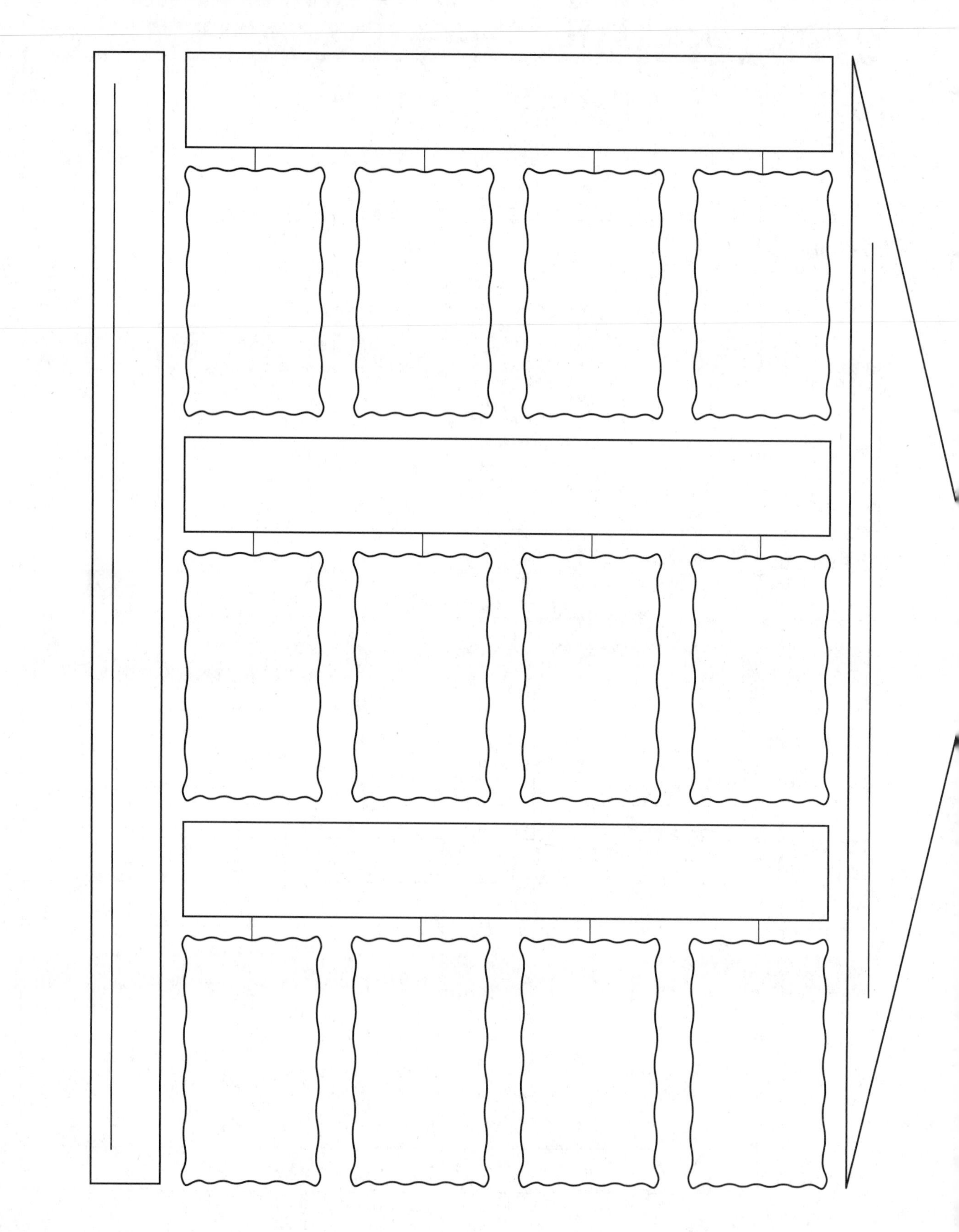

Color-Coded Blueprint for Writing

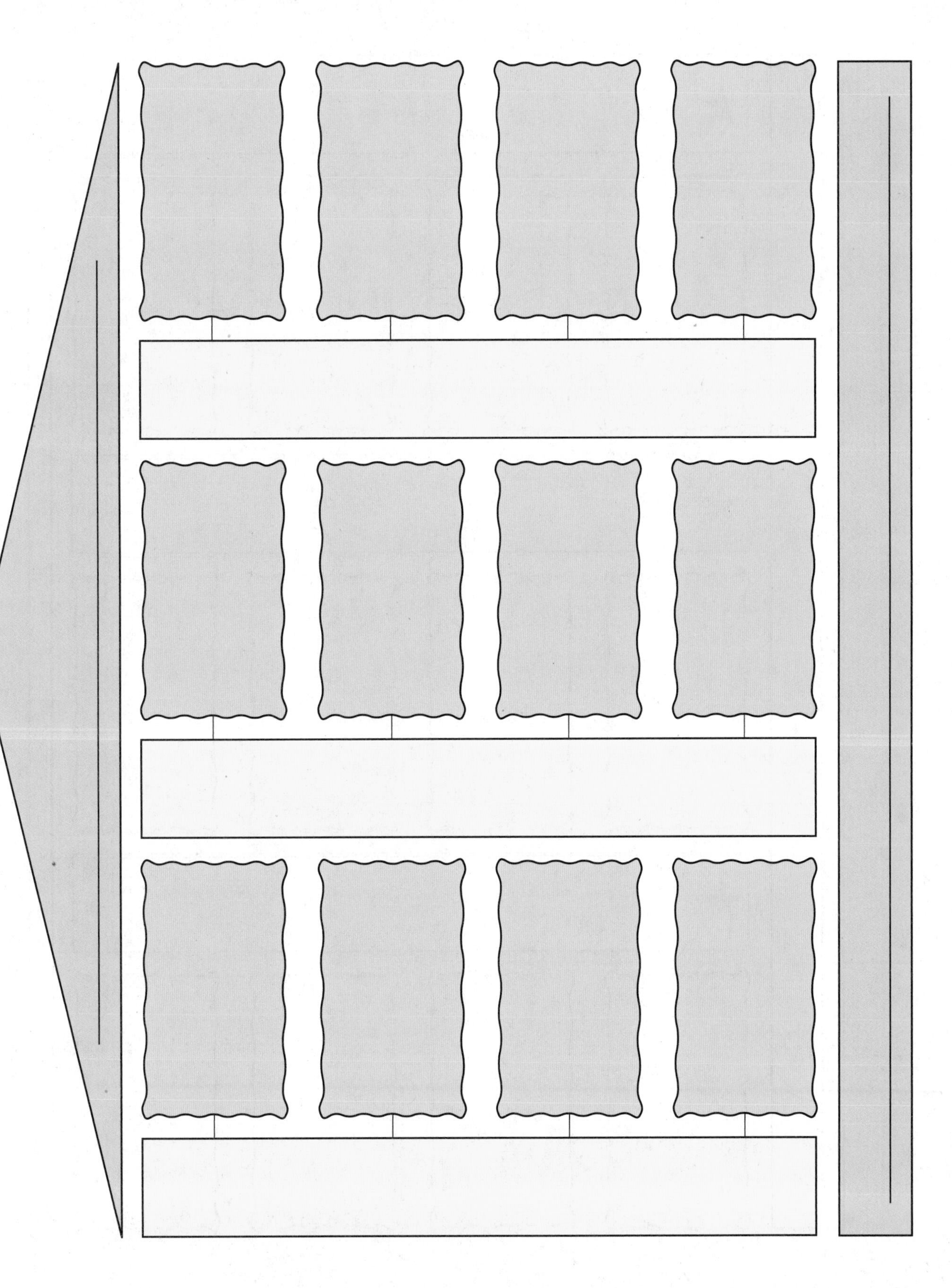

Blueprint for Writing With Symbols

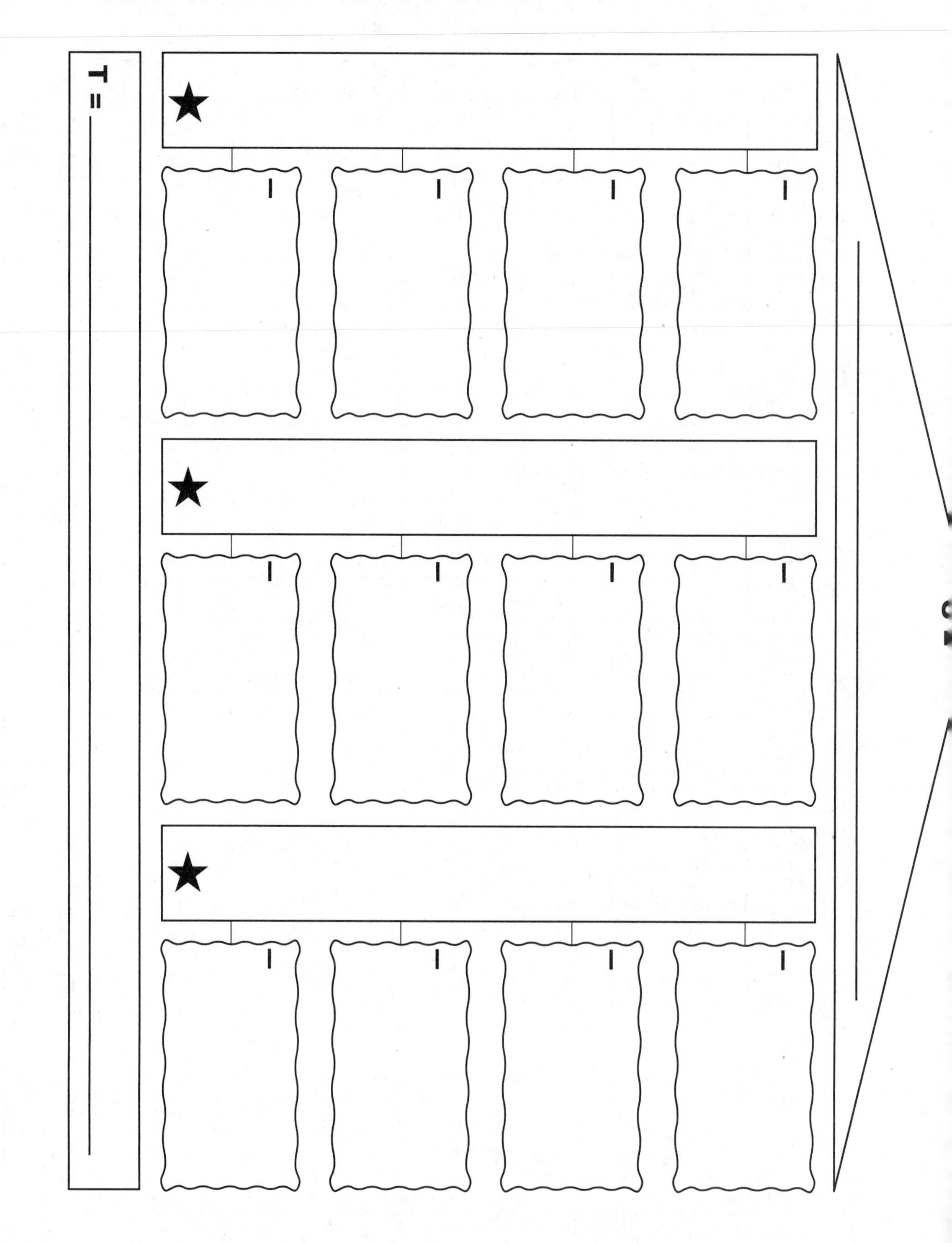

Copyright Acknowledgements

Batty About Bats
"Batty About Bats" by Kathiann Kowalski, from ODYSSEY, March 1999. © by Carus Publishing Company. Adapted and reproduced with permission.*

Africa Digs
"Finding the Pieces . . . and Putting Them Back Together Again" by Michelle Laliberte, from ODYSSEY, September 2000, Volume 9, Number 6. © by Carus Publishing Company. Adapted and reproduced with permission.*

Boston's Big Dig
"Big Dig" by Laurie Ann Toupin, from ODYSSEY, September 2003, Volume 11, Number 6. © by Carus Publishing Company. Adapted and reproduced with permission.*

Jazz: The Recipe
"Jazz Ingredients" by Heather Mitchell Amey, from COBBLESTONE, October 1983. © by Carus Publishing Company. Adapted and reproduced with permission.*

Coming Clean About Toxic Pollution
"Cleaner Cleaning" by Virginia Evarts Wadsworth, from COBBLESTONE, August 1989. © by Carus Publishing Company. Reproduced with permission.*

Rachel Carson
"Rachel Carson's World of Wonder" by Sylvia Salsbury, from APPLESEEDS, March 1999. © by Carus Publishing Company. Adapted and reproduced with permission.*

Photo and Illustration Credits

1: ©istockphoto.com/AZ. 4–5: © Merlin D. Tuttle/Bat Conservation International. 7: ©RGBStock.com/SatelliteW. 12: ©Anatoliy Samara/Dreamstime.com. 15: (baby) ©stock.xchng/sparkules; (couple) ©stock.xchng/izlomek; (shoes) ©Image Source; (sunset) ©stock.xchng/Peleda; (teacher) ©Getty Images/Ron Levine; (notebook) ©Getty Images/C Squared Studios; (calendar) ©stock.xchng; (watch) ©stock.xchng/ilco. 22: (cat) ©stock.xchng/Fred Fokkelman; (fish) ©Getty Images/Stephen Frink; (bat) ©istockphoto.com/Pasticcio; (baseball player) ©istockphoto.com/Matthew Brown. 29: (cat) ©stock.xchng/Marie Jeanne Lliescu; (bunny) ©stock.xchng/kjetilv; (runner) ©Getty Images/Alistair Berg; (dog) ©stock.xchng/Neil Watters. 41: (trowel) ©Wikipedia CC/Przemysław Sakrajda; (Niger map) ©Wikipedia CC/public domain; (Africa map) ©Wikipedia CC/public domain. 43–45: © Paul C. Sereno, courtesy Project Exploration. 46: ©1999–2003 Getty Images. 59: (girl) ©Szefei/Dreamstime.com; (children) ©stock.xchng/Seven Bates; (dune) ©stock.xchng/Sean Carpenter; (flood) ©stock.xchng.com/Greg Jordan. 83: (gemini) ©istockphoto.com/Sergey Mikhaylov; (background) ©Wikipedia CC/National Imagery and Mapping Administration. 85: ©Digital Stock. 87: *top.* ©istockphoto.com/Dan Mitchell; *middle.* ©istockphoto.com/Brett Lamb; *bottom.* ©istockphoto.com/Mosquito. 113: (cotton) ©istockphoto.com/David Sucsy; (notes) ©istockphoto.com/Bonnie Jacobs. 118: Illustrations: "Jazz Ingredients" by Heather Mitchell Amey, from COBBLESTONE, October 1983, Volume 4, Number 10. © by Carus Publishing Company. 138: *left.* ©Getty Images/Stockbyte; *right.* ©Getty Images/Digital Vision/Tony Anderson. 142: U.S. Navy photo by Photographer's Mate 1st Class Michael Worner. 161: ©istockphoto.com/ Antagain; (can) ©istockphoto.com/Somus. 163: ©Dynamic Graphics. 164: ©Getty Images/Digital Vision. 176: ©Wikipedia CC/U.S. Fish and Wildlife Service; (oyster) Illustration is from a 1902 Colorlitho by S. F. Denton. 190: ©stock.xchng/Mira Pavlakovic. 215, 217: ©istockphoto.com/Patricia Hofmeester. 218: ©Pictorial Parade/Getty. 239: ©istockphoto.com/ahlobystov. 244: ©stock.xchng.